Dr. William Reed, physician and surgeon, believes that Christianity offers unique and limitless potential for the understanding of the *whole* man, in illness and in health. He cites examples of actual cases that illustrate faith, or its lack, in the lives of sick people.

Dr. Reed believes—and has proven time and again—that the faith of the Christian can transform impossible situations into possible ones, darkness and hopelessness into light and optimism . . . and sickness into health.

Read here, see and believe what a living Christian faith can do!

SURGERY
OF THE SOUL

William Standish Reed, M.D.

SPIRE BOOKS

Fleming H. Revell Company   •   Old Tappan, New Jersey

SURGERY OF THE SOUL

A SPIRE BOOK
Published by Pyramid Publications for Fleming H. Revell Company

Second printing, February, 1975

Copyright © 1969 by Fleming H. Revell Company
All Rights Reserved

Library of Congress Catalog Card Number 77-85312

Printed in the United States of America

SPIRE BOOKS are published by Fleming H. Revell Company
Old Tappan, New Jersey 07675, U.S.A.

To my wonderful family and friends,
       especially Kay;
Ethel Tullock Banks,
       who led me to read Dr. Paul Tournier;
    and my university, the University of Michigan.

Contents

Introduction

WITH ALL OF the technological advances of modern medical science today, it is surprising to find American medicine working toward the spiritual in its consideration of man. Three decades ago the writings of Alexis Carrel created a furor and a storm in medical circles. Doctor Carrell along with Doctor Hugh Kelly of Johns Hopkins University and Doctor Richard Cabot of Harvard University were pioneers of a new, vital and much needed area of the practice of medicine and surgery as they looked beyond the treatment of the physical and the mental and considered deeply the spiritual in the treatment of the whole man.

Today committees on religion and medicine are common in American medical societies. Medicine is looking beyond the psychosomatic to the spiritual not only from the standpoint of the treatment of the individual patient but also in the consideration of etiology or the cause of illness and disease.

The purpose of this book is to give both physician and layman an opportunity to consider the great and relatively unexplored field of the human spirit in relationship to man's greatest enigma: consideration of himself. The religious and the spiritual in this book will be considered from the standpoint of Christianity, since the writer is a Christian and feels that, among all the religions, Christianity offers both patient and doctor the unique and limitless potential of understanding man when he is well and when he is sick. Christianity also uniquely gives man through Christ the power to perform both the possible and the impossible. This book is the product of twenty-three years of study. It is the product of a life which has been a mixture of victory and defeat. It is the product of a diligent search to try to understand man, particularly the sick man. It is offered only as a guide for further thought and contemplation. It will need modification in the future and much expansion.

My prayer is that it may be useful to both doctor and patient.

WILLIAM STANDISH REED, M.D.
Tampa, Florida

And this is the reason why the cure of many diseases is unknown to the physicians of Hellas, because they are ignorant of the whole, which ought to be studied also: for the part can never be well unless the whole is well.

Socrates

The fear of the Lord is the beginning of wisdom Psalms
111:10.

1-Beginnings

IT WAS A RATHER BLEAK, rainy night in the fall of 1939
when the bus in which I was a passenger pulled up in
front of the Men's Union and let me out into what was
to be the beginning of a great adventure. There was a
great sense of loneliness that evening, but this was
somewhat dispelled by the anticipation of entry into the
university. There were many reasons why I should not
have been there at all. Financial problems and physical
difficulties coupled to make it seem an almost insur-
mountable consideration. As I recall it now, there was
truly no defeatism in my attitude. I felt even then that I
was in God's hands, that it was really part of God's plan
for me to be walking along the rain-soaked, leaf-
covered street that night with nothing but hope in my
heart. No dormitory room had been provided and no
one was there to greet me. It was a matter of searching
out the address of an acquaintance to see if I could re-

main with him until I had obtained a room and hopefully a place of employment. Temporary quarters were soon obtained, and immediately I not only obtained a job which provided for my meals, but I also secured a paying position in the college symphony orchestra where I played the violin and viola. These endeavors and a job in the school of music library paid twelve dollars a month which, small though it may seem, paid for my room.

There were in the early years of my student days not only earnest strivings for knowledge but also a continuing quest for the inspiration of God in life and in study. As time went on the search for God became more dim, although He was always in my thinking. It seemed at that time that the churches I attended had very little message for me and student activities were often only social in their consideration. As burdens of study and work became greater, activities related to the church became less and less a part of my life. In 1942, when I entered medical school, most factors which had been present when I arrived were still constant and present, except that God and the inspiration of His Holy Spirit became less consciously apparent in my life. I recall the soul-searching which I did the day I entered the anatomy laboratory and considered what I, a human being, was actually doing in this life as I began to dissect the human body. I could not help reflecting upon the Psalmist's question, "What is man, that thou art mindful of him?" (Psalms 8:4). As time went on, all of us became hardened to the rigorous routine of medical school and insensitive to any spiritual consideration of our studies. The human body in its many functions, compositions and constituents was meticulously analyzed and studied from every possible standpoint except the spiritual. The psychological aspects of disease, the physiology and anatomy of the nervous system were carefully delved into; gradually we became experts in viewing man the machine with greater and greater knowledge. No matter what the motives my former classmates may have today for being in the practice of medicine, I feel confident that all of us at that time were interested in helping human beings. Our attitude was one of compassion, with a desire to understand and help them in their suffering. There was very little spiritual emphasis placed upon any of our studies during this growth process. I do feel certain that the tremendous integrity of the medical school's very inspiring teaching staff reflected upon each and every one of us students.

Internship was not appreciably different. Here again the work load was heavy, patient contact became a matter of routine, and the emphasis of our work with the individual patient was more upon his disease than upon the person who had the disease or abnormality.

The following years of experience in the Navy and in a civilian hospital found me absorbed in a desire to help people to the best of my ability as a physician. My approach was completely somatic, at best psychosomatic, giving very little thought to the spiritual aspect of patient care or the status of the patient or myself in relationship to God or to Christ.

A new world opened up to me during my training in a civilian hospital after leaving the U.S. Navy. There were the flickerings of something beyond the psychological and something beyond the somatic at that time. On one occasion, attempting to comfort the wife of a twenty-eight-year-old man who was dying of leukemia, I advised her to pray and told her that I myself would pray for her husband. This young man was one of the first patients to receive nitrogen mustard therapy at the hospital and as it was given it was administered with prayer not only from the wife and the recipient but also the young doctor who administered it. Despite all our efforts and prayers the patient died.

In another instance, a fifteen-year-old boy entered the hospital with terrible headaches and an inability to see with his right eye. Thorough studies by everyone had failed to reveal the cause of his problem. Spending much time with the patient and with his parents, I was able to determine that he had a very rare type of tumor which had spread to his brain. Here again, the only answer was to do all that we could medically and to point the family and the boy to Christ. In a fumbling way this was done and it became a sustaining force that allowed him to die victoriously and enabled his family to accept his death.

I remember a middle-aged man who was hysterically pushing the nurse's call button in his room because he was having severe chest pain. The nurses were all busy with other patients. Although the patient was on the medical service and I on the surgical service, his need called out to me. As I dashed into his room to discover his problem, he stated that he was having tremendous pain. Not only did he state his problem, but he cursed at me because of his anger at not being served as soon as he thought he should be.

From a nurse I obtained the necessary medication; I ran to his bedside, hurriedly applying a tourniquet to his arm, attempting to find a vein in which to inject narcotic to ease his pain! The nurse was frantically trying to contact his doctor. Because of the patient's violence, his cursing and his irascibility, I could not find the vein in which to inject the medication. In the midst of this violent psychological reaction of hatred toward me and toward everyone because of our failure to please him, the man collapsed and died in my arms. I saw at that time the terrible penalty which hatred and violence can cause in an individual life.

These were but beginnings, experiences, considerations, thoughts all pointing toward a future in which, based upon a philosophy of practice and a foundation of ethical reality, I could begin my own medical practice. I decided that the highest calling of the physician should be that of general practitioner. I thought that such a man would cover the broad spectrum of people's needs without the narrowness and the gun barrel vision sometimes associated with one who cannot see beyond his specialty.

Choose you this day whom ye will serve Joshua 24:15.

2- The Choice

GENERAL PRACTICE was a most happy and enlightening experience. A small town G.P. becomes very much a member of the community and a close member of the families whom he treats. He may not be admired from the standpoint of the profession in general because his education is not as prolonged as the specialist's, but the general practitioner must be a man of unusual abilities and insights. It has always seemed a strange paradox to me that the man in medicine who needs the greatest knowledge of all has the shortest period of training, and the man who needs knowledge in a very narrow segment of medicine or surgery has years of training before he enters practice. It has been my observation that the general practitioner is often the real doctor and the specialist is often a superior mechanic in a narrow field.

When he enters practice the general practitioner finds that there are very subtle pressures exerted to require him to specialize, if he is going to be able to help his patients in the way he would most desire. There was a time when most babies were delivered by general practitioners. In many areas the general practitioner now may not be allowed to deliver babies, or he is only allowed to do so under the supervision of a specialist. There was a time when much of the surgery which was performed was done by general practitioners; specialists in the large centers performed only the most complicated forms of surgery. Now, in many areas, general practitioners are not allowed to do anything but very minor surgery. These factors cause the young general practitioner to practice only long enough to decide what field of specialty he desires to enter. Then he leaves his practice to become a specialist.

Thus it was for me when I found in my general practice that many of the simple surgical conditions which confronted me day to day were successfully handled as I operated upon them. However, as specialization became more a rule of the day, I began to see that, in order to be able to do surgery at all, it was going to be necessary for me to specialize. Leaving one's practice, the families he has grown to love, the babies he has delivered, and those he has helped through victories and defeats—these are difficult things to face. However, it was with great joy that I again entered university life with all its new challenges and opportunities. The surgical training itself was a strict discipline, leaving little time for either sleep or social activity. There was the constant inspiration of the professors and others surrounding us in the various hospital departments which made every moment exhilarating and challenging.

My chief was a man able to probe deeply into the inner depths of his patients and his residents. He ne-

glected no aspect of his patient, including the spiritual.
He exemplified the personal approach to the patient and
instructed his interns and residents to comfort the patient as well as to take care of him professionally. He
represented not only the surgeon as scientist but also as
counselor, friend, and minister in the deepest sense of
the word. Four years of training under him and his
staff passed as a day, and although the opportunity was
presented for me to stay on, I elected to get back to my
former friends of general practice days, to catch up the
loose ends and renew friendships.

During my years of training at the university I had
developed a close relationship with one of the professors of pathology. It was she who had asked me one day
if I felt that Jesus Christ could heal anyone today. It
was she who suggested that we study the spiritual aspect
of patient care. It was she who again kindled a little fire
in what had been only a flickering spark in my spiritual
life. As a result of the discussions and investigation
which we conducted, I left the university not only as a
trained surgeon, but also as a person considering more
and more deeply the spiritual aspect of patient care.

As the realization deepened of how powerful the force
of prayer could be in one's life and the life of his patients, I began to pray for my patients and for those in
my acquaintance who were ill. I began to see that man
himself is a very limited being. As he begins to see his
own limitations, he looks about him viewing with increasing sensitivity the limitations of those about him.
When man contemplates God, he tends to limit Him,
measuring God by the same yardstick which he uses to
measure himself. He does not see God in His limitless-
ness, in all of His influences upon man.

In this limited context, one might believe that God

sends illness upon man, perhaps as a result of his sin, perhaps as the result of his being in an environment of sin in this world. This is a difficult belief for the physician: if God does in truth send disease, the physician is fighting against God as he makes man well. If, however, disease is a result of sin and of evil primarily, the physician is in a very comforting place as he works with God as his co-laborer, striving to destroy illness and, hopefully, the sin which causes it. It was with considerations such as these, coupled with a thorough training in surgery, that I re-entered practice, vowing to incorporate to the greatest extent possible the spiritual principles which I had just begun to perceive as real and absolutely necessary. There was to come a time of growth and of struggle as well as times of heartbreak and discouragement. One does not lightly place himself on God's road, because such a decision carries with it not only the potential of the miraculous but also the possibility of misunderstanding.

Having worked with cancer patients and patients with other diseases which medical science views as incurable, I felt strongly at the inception of surgical practice that the most neglected area of research and of thought is the spiritual. Is it possible that many illnesses have a spiritual cause? If this area of the causation of disease is true, perhaps the correction of spiritual factors can cause the healing of illnesses which by any other means would not be possible.

What was present then, as the specialty practice of surgery began, was not only the scientific consideration of man but also a deepening interest in the spiritual as well as the psychological. Man cannot be seen as a strictly surgical entity or medical consideration; he must be seen as a whole being. He cannot be visualized purely as a physical being, since triune man does not exist in separate compartments. The mental cannot be isolated from the physical. This has been proved by the multiple researches and experiences in psychosomatic medicine.

We have made the error of believing that the psychological and the spiritual are one and the same. Biblically, man is divided into three parts. "And the very God of peace sanctify you wholly; and *I pray God* your whole spirit and soul and body be preserved blameless unto the coming of our Lord Jesus Christ" (I Thessalonians 5:23). "For the word of God *is* quick, and powerful, and sharper than any two-edged sword, piercing even to the dividing asunder of soul and spirit, and of the joints and marrow, and *is* a discerner of the thoughts and intents of the heart" (Hebrews 4:12). It is a mistake, then, to consider soul and spirit to be one and the same; and it is also a mistake to consider the psychological synonymous with the spiritual. Throughout this book man will be considered to be a logo-psychosomatic being: that is, spirit, soul, and body. Soul and mind will be considered to be one and the same.

In the beginning, during the development of the physician, man is seen as an unending world of fascinating facts and wondrous characteristics. Gradually, material concepts of man fade to those of an even greater world comprising the unending depths of the study and the productivity of the mind. Beyond this lies the unexplored. To date only theologians have given it much consideration at all, and they have been bound by limitations of dogma, creed, and denomination. Is this a realm too far removed from the physician's consideration? Or does it, like outer space and the universe, represent a challenge which he can investigate? Can such investigation obtain facts which will, in the years to come, help man not only to understand himself, but also to achieve new insights into prevention and treatment of all forms of illness?

And the Lord said to Cain, Where is Abel your brother?
Genesis 4:9. THE AMPLIFIED BIBLE.

3-Discipline

CURRENT SURGICAL thought is highly scientific and technical, bearing few of the earmarks of the philosophy of surgical practice which formerly characterized surgery as an art as well as a science. Before the new resident surgeon there looms the great challenge: to help suffering humanity by applying diligently the skills learned from teachers and from study. With heart-lung machines, respirators, dacron prostheses, hypotensive anaesthesia, controlled respiration, controlled cardiac arrest, and many technical devices and procedures, the surgeon tends to become a super-technician, a statistician, an operator or a research coordinator, a reader of multitudes of articles, a writer or perhaps even more, a working machine. The demands upon the surgeon are staggering and ever-increasing. Soon after becoming established in the practice of medicine, he finds himself in a dilemma. How does one do all that is required of him surgically and scientifically and still maintain his intellect, his soul, his spirit, his family, his religion, his faith? How does the surgeon who sees on every hand the wondrous working power of God integrate his Christian faith into his surgical practice? Is there truly a place for God in this new technical world of scientific discipline? Inevitably, also, to the young surgeon comes the question, "What is to be done now when nothing surgically or technically can be done?"—as in the patient with carcinomatosis or multiple myeloma or a myriad of other disorders for which we still stand by helpless to do anything curative?

There are certain moral precepts in surgery which are more religious than they are scientific. One of these is the aim of the doctor: "To cure sometimes, to relieve often, to comfort always." Another is the rule of the surgeon: if he cannot do anything to help, he must do no harm. The Oath of Hippocrates states: "In honesty and purity I will live my life and practice my art." The surgeon may differ from ordinary man by virtue of education, knowledge, ability, and affluence. He must also ask himself as any other man, when considering a possible action aimed at another human being, "If I were in his situation, how would I wish to be treated?"

"The second [commandment] is like unto it [the first], Thou shalt love thy neighbor as thyself" (Matthew 22:39). As doctor cares for patient with skill and concern, he is being truly religious, according to the definition of St. James. "Pure religion and undefiled before God and the Father is this, To visit the fatherless and widows in their affliction" (James 1:27). "Where is Abel thy brother?" (Genesis 4:9).

Surgery, although a science, must never be divorced from its true place as a deep philosophical discipline, closer to the spirit of man than the sacred ministry itself. The surgeon, perhaps even more than the internist or psychiatrist, deals with the deep things in the lives of men. The operating room is more than a place where certain technical things are done to men to make them well or to restore function: it is a place where lives hang suspended between life and death. There the soul sleeps, the body is insensible, and the spirit hovers in communion with God. In the hands of surgeon and anaesthesiologist lie not only a life, but soul and spirit capable of being influenced for good or for evil by word or thought or act.

In Judaism there occurs a question asked in the prayer of everyone, teacher or layman, "Do you know before *Whom* you stand?" Could we in surgery not well afford to ask ourselves, "Do you know with Whom you operate? Do you know before Whom you stand?"

Not only is the operating theatre an area to consider in the Medicine of the Person, but also the patient's room; consultation and examining rooms are important also. Here as well contact occurs between doctor and patient on all three levels: body, mind, and spirit. The surgeon must never consider lightly the great trust the patient bestows upon him when he places his life and his future into his hands. Here is an act of trust which surpasses any act of surrender of one individual to another in all the drama of life. Without the consideration of soul and spirit, surgery becomes mere technology.

Even a surgeon who considers his actions toward his patient from a purely technical viewpoint cannot escape the fact that the patient affects the doctor himself on all three levels of the doctor's being: his spirit, soul, and body. Being a doctor carries with it not only honor, rewards, applause, and position; being a doctor also places the individual physician at center target of thoughts and fears, loves, hopes, anger, disappointment and a multitude of other emotions constantly beamed at him from patients. The development of detached professional impersonality has become the new demeanor of many physicians. This frame of professional life is not a protection against the patient-doctor relationship effect, because the doctor is in the midst of a triune relationship which cannot be escaped or sidestepped. It is a part of medical and surgical practice, and we are involved with our patient—his spirit, his soul, and his body—whether we desire to be or not. He is similarly involved with us; and both of us are involved with God.

When the physician sees the deeper meaning of life and of his practice, every aspect of his work takes on a wonderful new dimension. How splendid it is to save life, to restore function. How much greater—by act or word or witness—also to give meaning to that life through the Lord Jesus Christ! What would happen if the physician, whose flesh, blood, and soul are the same as his patient should suddenly begin to see patients as eternal beings whose needs are spiritual as well as mental and physiological? No physician would deny the need to consider man as a psychosomatic entity. How can one divorce the psychosoma from the spirit? When this is done, medicine deteriorates into a mechanical science with an occasional nod toward Sigmund Freud. The physician is taught to be a doctor first, a specialist second. As a doctor he must see the total need of the whole person and treat him accordingly. This means listening to his problem; sitting down and conversing with him, and praying with him. The concept of the whole man means more than the theoretical admission of the existence of the various aspects of the human being or of God. It means being a whole doctor ministering to the total need of the whole patient.

It is my position at this point to state that our patient cannot become whole without Jesus Christ. There is no other philosophical system or religion which gives honor to the eternal spirit of man or which shows him the means of personal salvation and the way to wholeness and to life eternal which compares in any way to Christianity. We who read scientific literature to such a demanding degree should realize that great insight into the persons of our patients and ourselves can be derived through the reading and study of the Holy Bible. Jesus Christ has much to say to us, the physicians of today.

Medical ethics have become mere rules of conduct between doctors themselves and their patients, cold— lifeless—impersonal! Jesus Christ gives to medical ethics their true place, taking into consideration the eternal spirit and man's relationship to God. Jesus' teachings are truly more a part of our medical thinking than we know. His principles are actually more the principles of medical ethics than are the tenets of Hippocrates. The ethics of medicine have more to do with interpersonal relationships than other such considerations as fee-splitting or ghost surgery. Such rules have become necessary because of the deterioration of medicine into a job, a means of income, a way to affluence. Materialistic medicine, emphasizing values other than honor and love of fellow man, slowly resolves into a means of maintaining self-esteem, position, income, and status. It largely ignores the Church, the Hippocratic oath, and traditional values. The Medicine of the Whole Person relates doctor and patient to Christ, who teaches man who he really is and how patient as well as physician can become whole.

Medicine as a field of scientific endeavor requires discipline in life and study. The Medicine of the Whole Person imposes an even deeper discipline upon the life and practice of the physician. Such a discipline requires that the patient's humanity never be forgotten, and that the patient's relationship to God never be violated. Such a concept of medical and surgical practice places a greater honor upon the individual patient than is usual, and requires a deeper discipline of life and of thought on the part of the doctor. Jesus Christ, the Great Physician, shows us both, doctor and patient, the way to accomplish this life-giving, creative, and redemptive relationship.

For the Word that God speaks is alive and full of power— making it active, operative, energizing and effective; it is sharper than any two-edged sword, penetrating to the dividing line of the breath of life (soul) and [the immortal] spirit, and of joints and marrow Hebrews 4:12 THE AMPLIFIED BIBLE.

4-Freedom of Life

AS A PHYSICIAN, my interpretation of this verse would be, "For the Word of God is alive and full of power and sharper than any two-edged sword (knife), cutting even to the dissection and separation of man's soul from his spirit, of his joints from his marrow."

Every man, no matter what his vocation, profession, or lot in life, must, at one time or another, answer the question Jesus put to the Pharisees, "What think ye [of Christ]?" (Matthew 22:42). This question the individual must pose to himself; it is asked far more often than is supposed. The concerns of a busy residency in a large hospital veritably keep one from thinking as deeply as he ought about what he is doing, particularly with reference to his fellow man and to his God. This was very true of me, and perhaps Jesus' question would have gone unanswered had I not been asked the searching question, "Do you believe that Jesus Christ heals today?"

Confronted with this question, it is necessary to answer. To be neutral is to deny. There was no definite reason for affirming except that deep within I had always carried the conviction that God *is* the Author of health and wholeness; therefore, Jesus, who is the perfect reflection of God, did heal the sick when He was on earth and does heal the sick today through His disciples.

Thus affirming, I concluded, "If we believe this, why don't we study it?" Thus began a long period of exploration running concurrently with medical-surgical studies. Through this period of endeavor I was introduced to the Medicine of the Person through the writings of Paul Tournier, M.D. Encounter with Tournier and his presentation of Christ in the practice of medicine became the turning point in my life. It was he whom God used to point me toward the Bible as well as to Christ. The Bible was God's scalpel, cutting me free from materialism.

God's Word, the Holy Bible, is life itself, possessing unlimited power. It has tremendous potential and is of such a character that it has the ability to cut, to dissect and to separate even man's soul from his spirit. Ordinarily, the soul of man is considered to be the same as his spirit. Many Scriptural references could be used to show that the soul of man actually is comparable not to his spirit but to his mind. The Greek word *psuche* is the same as our word psyche, used in such words as psychological, psychiatric, pertaining to mind. Thus we see that in order to understand the statement, we must see that there is a difference between the soul and the spirit. Man's spirit doubtless exists in embryonic or atrophic form until the Holy Spirit brings it to life at the time of his conversion. It then begins to grow as it is nurtured by the Holy Spirit and the Word of God as well as by Christian living. It is this part of man which is eternal. Conversely, if the spirit of man is taken over by evil, it grows in a perverse direction as it is nurtured by the forces of evil which come upon him through the thoughts, words, and deeds of the world. The Word of God has the potential of cutting between the psychological aspect of man and his spirit, thus setting free the spirit from the soul. As man progresses in intellectuality and in knowledge he develops a tendency to subvert his spirit. God's Word presents Jesus Christ, who was able to liberate man's spirit from its incarceration by the intellect.

In the beginning, Eve was deceived by Satan through an attack upon her intellect. Jesus Christ makes it possible to subvert the intellect, making the spirit primary. The mind of Christ becomes our potential, liberating our spirits so that we can in truth be like Him. "Let this mind be in you, which was also in Jesus Christ" (Philippians 2:5). "For if we have been planted together in the likeness of his death, we shall be also *in the likeness of his* resurrection" (Romans 6:5). Such elevation of spirit neither destroys nor diminishes man's intellectuality. Actually, such a choice expands his mental processes. To ordinary intellectual powers he has the added gifts of the Holy Spirit, including knowledge and wisdom (I Corinthians 12:8). Intellectual knowledge does not liberate. Man is freed through the Holy Spirit revealed through God's Word.

Interesting also is the statement in Hebrews 4:12 that the Bible has the ability to cut between the joints and the marrow. As a surgeon it is difficult to understand how this could possibly be, because the marrow of the bones is not in continuity with the joints. If St. Paul had said "the cutting away of the cartilage from the bone" or "the bone from the marrow," it might be more understandable. Certainly there is no anatomic problem in separating of the joints from the marrow. There must be a deeper meaning here. No person would be able to walk or function without his joints. In order for a person to be healthy it is important for him to be able to move freely and to do so he must have normal joints. The joints cannot be arthritic or frozen in order for one to have proper function and mobility. The joints thus bespeak freedom. For a person to be healthy and to have life he must have healthy marrow. The marrow produces the cellular elements of the blood. Certain drugs act upon the marrow and cause it to be unable to produce blood elements. Certain anemias are caused by a lack of functioning marrow. Patients with anemia are weak and lifeless because of the lack of blood cells. Thus the marrow bespeaks life.

The joints of man indicate freedom, particularly freedom of motion, and the bone marrow bespeaks life. The Bible creates a means of cutting man free from the world and from the artificial aspects of the worldly life. In so doing he is completely liberated into the freedom of the Spirit. He is also given life even unto the very marrow of his bones as the life of Christ, who is Life, is infused into every area of his being. Jesus Christ, as revealed in the Bible, gives to men who will accept Him as Saviour the means of liberation and the way to life in contrast to captivity and death which are the products of life without Him.

See, I have set before thee this day life and good, and death and evil Deuteronomy 30:15.

5-Decision

APPLICATION of Christian principles to the practice of medicine and surgery is a difficult consideration when viewed from a practical aspect. As long as it remains on the level of the theoretical, Christianity never creates problems. Difficulties ensue when the vital principles of true Christianity are applied to life. As long as man is considered strictly a psychosomatic being and as long as the spiritual is excluded from the consideration of doctor and hospital, there are few problems. When the spiritual aspect of man is considered not just by the hospital chaplain but by the surgeon, and when application is made of the principles of Jesus Christ to the surgeon's life and practice, misunderstandings and questions may ensue.

John Watson, the Scottish clergyman, once wrote concerning the cross of Christ, "The cross is wrought in gold and hung from the neck of light-hearted beauty; it stands out in bold relief on churches that are filled with easygoing people. The cross has been taken out of Jesus' hands and smothered with flowers; it has become what He would have hated, a source of graceful ideas and agreeable emotions. When Jesus presented the cross to His disciples, He was certainly not thinking of a sentiment which can disturb no man's life nor redeem any man's soul, but of the unsightly beams which must be set up in the midst of man's pleasures and the jagged nails which must pierce his soul." The decision to believe in Jesus Christ involves the acceptance of the cross.

In the application of vital Christianity to a scientific discipline such as surgery, there are bound to be conflicts and difficulties. Many present-day surgeons would state that surgery is a scientific discipline *per se,* having no element beyond the scientific in any sense. However, we are dealing with human beings who cannot be viewed from strictly physiological, Freudian, or evolutionary points of view. Man remains indefinable and the complexity of his being increases with every new facet of knowledge.

A surgeon in Canada viewed with deep despair a young adult man dying of melanoma, metastatic to his liver. The liver had become so large that it filled the entire right side of the abdomen; the patient was extremely ill, requiring frequent blood transfusions. Suddenly one day, following prayer by a group of concerned individuals, the patient began improving, the liver decreased in size, and finally became normal. The patient then began a complete recovery and has been well to this day.

How can one define what happened in such a case? What is there about man on the level of the spiritual which allows him to respond in such a way to prayer?

Admittedly, this does not always happen, nor is it a frequent occurrence. However, such things do occur, not only on the level of individual prayer, but at healing shrines such as Lourdes and through the ministries of certain Christian ministers. Medicine must take a closer look into these areas.

The doctor who uses chemotherapy in the all-too-often vain hope of prolonging life must give thought in other directions, including the area of Christian Healing. If we are to consider ourselves open-minded and willing to experiment on the level of the pragmatic, i.e., with drugs and destructive surgery, radiation therapy, and similar related fields of cancer therapy where success is limited, certain Christian investigators must think also in the direction of The Medicine of the Whole Person. Medicine must become more open in this direction, since startling healings of incurable illnesses continue to occur through the Ministry of Christian Healing.

Life itself is impossible to explain. Even on the level of simple viruses, we have become expert in the description of the biologic and chemical phenomena, but we have not been able to go beyond observation. The more minute our observations of man, the more amazed we become at the complexity and the wonder of him.

Certain ground rules have become firmly established in the realm of metabolic and physio-chemical factors. No surgeon could even begin to consider the performance of major surgery on a patient without a thorough knowledge of the metabolic balance and a multitude of related factors. However, it is amazing to note that the end results of therapy in such a condition as carcinoma of the breast are little better than the results of William

Halsted at the turn of the century! Perhaps it is time for the researchers to expand their horizons to include a consideration of the spiritual, not only in the treatment of the sick individual but in the prevention of physical and psychological illness. This requires something beyond launching an ordinary scientific investigation. No man can investigate these realms without first thoroughly coming to an understanding of himself and his relationship to God through Jesus Christ. One cannot approach God trusting in his own righteousness or in an attitude other than humility.

St. Paul's letter to the Corinthians can be paraphrased from the point of view of the practitioner of medicine. Such a paraphrase makes one see how medicine, or any area of life, could be oriented toward a higher path.

1. Though my tongue be endued with the speech of angels with absolute completeness in all areas of man's intellectuality, and though I should speak with the inspired genius of my profession but lack the compassion of Christ, I am in reality but a hollow sounding, chiming cymbal.

2. Though I be endowed with the deepest insight and diagnostic intuition added to a rational grasp of causes and cures of human disease; although I have superior skills in the surgical ability to excise diseased organs and tissues; although I can bind up broken bodies and minds, if I lack compassion for human suffering, I am ineffectual as a conveyor of life and preserver of wholeness.

3. Though I invest all my substance in the cause of research, even allowing my own body to be dissected in the anatomy laboratory, if I do not have divine compassion it profits me nothing.

4. The deep and sacrificial love of a doctor for his patients causes physical and emotional suffering, but the good physician's life never loses its kindness. In this deep love there is no envy, no pride, no self-esteem.

5. In this deeper aspect of professional life there is no disorderliness; there is no seeking after the aims and objectives of self or of professional groups or societies. There is no easy provocation to anger and evil thoughts toward one's self or others are dispelled.

6. There is no joy because of the evil or ill happening to colleagues or others, but there is great rejoicing when truth is expounded and when Jesus, who is the Truth, is lifted up. Deep love toward colleague and patient is able to bear all problems and all joys. It allows a continuing belief in the good. Not only is it accompanied by the giving forth of hope to all patients, no matter how serious their disease, but it forbids hopelessness even in the life of the doctor himself. Come what may, the life of God's love is able to endure all.

7. God's love never fails, but though there be great scientific lectures on all manner of disease

phenomena and though there be all manner of intellectual pursuits, these shall eventually be no longer necessary. Inspired utterances in one's own devotional life or in the church or public meeting, even these shall eventually disappear. In the realm of professional knowledge and all of the areas of scientific advancement, present and future, in the divine scheme of things these too eventually will pass away. For now we only have a partial knowledge and in this knowledge, we can see only a part of what is true.

8. When Jesus comes again with all of His perfection, our partial methods will evaporate as the dew before the rising sun, for His completeness shall reveal it all.

9. Despite all professional attainments and all the knowledge which we can accumulate in this short span of our years, we are but children in our learning and in our abilities, compared with what shall be eventually revealed in us. Therefore, we must see that we speak but as children and have limited understanding in our immaturity. We think as children do, but as we achieve the maturity which is full manhood (body, soul, and spirit), our childish and immature areas are put away, through Jesus' own perfection working in us.

10. We get but little glimpses of the light of Christ in this present darkness, but soon when Jesus comes we shall see Him face to face and His Truth shall be revealed.

11. So in our professional lives, as we have faith in Him and as we give faith to those who are our patients and our colleagues, let us always be conveyors of hope, abounding in hope and abounding in the sacrificial Love of Jesus. Of these three values, let us remember that above all there is the deep and continuing love of God Himself, which dwells in these vessels of clay, our bodies, in which His Holy Spirit abides —if we but will Him so to do.

Jesus said unto her, I am the resurrection, and the life: he that believeth in me, though he were dead, yet shall he live John 11:25.

6-Cancer I

THE PATIENT was a young woman, a piano teacher in her home community, who had noticed the small nodule in her breast. Since she was a believer in the Gospel of Jesus Christ, she and her friends agreed that she should pray about her abnormality and seek medical help later. Such was her mode of care. She ignored her problem and went along without concern. Within two months, she saw a physician on another matter and the mass in the breast was discovered. The physician advised her to have immediate surgery. She declined.

Many months went by during which time the mass grew to involve the entire breast. It became inflammatory and the lymph nodes began to enlarge in the axilla. Shortly thereafter she began to have small hemorrhages from the breast. This was very debilitating. Eventually, a fellow townsman prevailed upon her to seek medical advice. An ambulance carried her across the state to receive surgical help.

When the patient arrived multiple transfusions were necessary before it was possible to even evaluate her condition. Examination revealed an advanced cancer of the breast. In order to control the bleeding it was necessary to take her to the operating room and to remove the breast.

The patient did well following her surgery for a time, but eventually developed recurrences in the skin and in the lungs. After many months of distress, during which her only solace was prayer and her deep belief in the Lord Jesus Christ, the patient died.

The reason for detailing this patient's history is simply to indicate that it is not a manifestation of faith for a person to ignore obvious surgical indications because he feels that he is trusting God by not going to a doctor. The first thing for a patient to do whenever he has a physical abnormality of any sort is to pray and perhaps to ask the Christian community to pray for him. He then should seek his physician and follow whatever advice that physician gives. In the instance quoted above, the patient should have sought help from her physician immediately and should have had surgery as well as prayer. Had she done this, she no doubt could have been well today. Neglect is not faith. Admittedly, we do not have in medicine or surgery today the answer to the cancer problem. However, this does not mean that we should not take advantage of the knowledge that we do have. We are able to give the patient considerably more help if he is operated upon, than he would have if he neglects himself. The sooner one gets medical help or surgical help when he has cancer, the more chance he has of surviving this illness, which is so common today.

Not long ago a woman who had cancer of the breast wrote to me. Her letter indicates the proper approach and a most interesting example of the way in which Jesus heals the person who seeks medical advice and yet gets into difficulty.

Dear Dr. Reed,

Last March, our sixth baby was born on Easter morning. She was a beautiful girl. (My husband and I felt very blessed of the Lord for our family—now we had five girls, one boy, all of them healthy and perfect. I had had good health, no complications, natural childbirth, and had been able to nurse each one.) It was a little upsetting to discover a mass in one breast, and while in the hospital, my "Gyn" man called in a surgeon. He advised a biopsy right away, but after consideration and seeing how disappointed I was at the prospect of stopping nursing, he felt reasonably sure it was a plugged gland. For the next eight months, it neither enlarged nor became sensitive—the surgeon checked it regularly. After I finished nursing, it did not go away, so he recommended minor surgery—probably a cyst.

I entered the hospital. After surgery, I woke up with two thoughts: there had been a lapse of time, and never had I known so much pain. Then my husband told me—yes, it was seven hours later, there had been radical breast removal, but the surgeon was very reassuring. It had been a plugged gland after all; but sensing something, he had discovered a pea-sized malignant tumor, in no way connected with the origi-

nal problem and was forced to do a mastecto-
my. He was certain he had removed it all.

It was interesting that I had a memory of great
pain, but it was not the pain I was having at the
present time. I was still under sedation. My recovery was rapid—returned home in ten days
and in a month had almost full use of my arm.
But deep inside I was very troubled. I remember
just before Christmas I rode along in the car as
the rest of the family went on the traditional
hike at the tree farm to pick out our Christmas
tree. As I watched them go, I choked back the
tears and tried desperately to repress the idea
that this was the last year with my family—I
had better take each view in completely. Many
nights I would wake up knowing that I had had
a very disturbing nightmare, but never being
able to recall what it was about.

The doctor had advised a hysterectomy as pre-
ventive medicine, so in January I had a pan-
hysterectomy. Recovery again was very rapid,
lab reports had all been negative, and truly we
were rejoicing. But the nightmares continued
and the last one I remembered vividly. I
dreamed while my husband and I were sleeping
that a sinister figure, dressed in white, with a
cloth wrapped around his head, entered our
room, came to the head of the bed and started
talking to me. I knew I should tell Bob that this
evil man was here. I dreamed I was shaking Bob
to wake up, was trying to tell him, but could
make only guttural sounds. Actually this *was*
happening. Bob woke up, heard the grunts I was
making. I could hear him talking to me and say-

ing to wake up, but I couldn't respond. It seemed like a long time, but was only moments until I awoke and could tell him of the nightmare.

Four weeks after the hysterectomy, I returned for an examination: everything had gone so well, I asked the doctor how he felt about recurrence and was stunned as I heard the words coming out, "Medically we offer you no hope. Metastasis has taken place . . . cancer in one ovary . . . perhaps you'll have as long as two years." This was on a Wednesday afternoon.

Thursday morning I called a friend and asked her to pray for us. I had really been shattered inside. She said that she and her husband had been trying to contact my husband, for they heard via the grapevine that the surgeon during the radical had said this was serious, and he'd give me a year to live. That shattered me more to think he had not told me the truth. Actually, eighteen nodes had been removed, many of them involved.

Friday I called my doctor on the phone, for I remembered they had taken a series of X-ray pictures in the hospital. Had they shown anything further? "Yes, it was also in the lower spine."

That was the lowest night of my life. After many tears, deep soul-searching, and review of our lives together, Bob and I came to several conclusions. We were still young—thirty-five, and our children were still young, the oldest eleven. We had had a very deep and meaningful relationship as husband and wife, and although we really didn't want all this to end this way, we still were willing to have the Lord's will in our lives. And even if we didn't understand all this, in faith we believed our total commitment to Christ included even this.

Saturday the doctor called and said there was a disagreement on the diagnosis of the X-ray; they did not now see it in the lower spine. Good news, yes, but I have to admit I was so shattered emotionally that I was very nauseated and had lost weight rapidly those three days.

We asked if our pastor and elders would come and pray for us. On Sunday they came, and while this has not been a practice in our church, they anointed me with oil, had laying on of hands, and a very meaningful and precious time in prayer for healing. My nausea went away and has never returned!

Along with the battle of being willing to give total commitment came the small beginning of faith to be healed. As an encouragement, I had asked the Lord to heal rapidly three dime-size spots on the large skin graft that had not changed for nine weeks. By the next morning they were beginning to dry up and in one and a half weeks were completely healed! This, plus the prayer by our pastor and elders, helped me much during the next two weeks. It seems like a real spiritual battle to resist fear and discouragement and hang on to faith to believe for healing. It was as real as Satan confronting me and speaking, "You think you are healed? Why should you be healed when people are dying from cancer every day? What about this pain in

your back?" And then I would get an over-
whelming pain in my back. This would happen
over and over and the only way to combat it
would be to pray, "Lord, I know I don't deserve
to be healed, but You have been giving me faith
to believe for healing. Now, I don't know what
this pain is, but I just give it to You to deal with.
Anything of fear or depression is not from You
—You give peace and joy!" I cannot even begin
to evaluate the help from the prayers of our
Christian friends at this time.

After two weeks of this, in the middle of a
day, a sense of someone saying, "Now don't
concentrate on so much of the physical, for the
heat of the battle is over," swept over me. It was
not a rebuke—more a guiding thing. And it was
over!

A week or so later another thing very unexpect-
ed, strange, but very real, happened. I know
God deals differently with people. We are all
different and individuals. I can't explain it. I just
know it happened to me. I was lying down rest-
ing one afternoon, dully awake, when I was im-
pressed with a strong picture in my mind. A
line, broken in the middle, a dark black ugly
mass boiling up and spilling out at the break,
and the word CANCER above. I had never experienced anything like this and thought it was
just my imagination—maybe I should just think
of something else. But it wouldn't go away. So I
looked at it clearly and it changed then to an
unbroken line with the words beneath, AS IF IT
HAD NEVER BEEN.

I particularly noticed that I couldn't see where

the break had been—no scar to show me. I jumped off the bed overwhelmed with the closeness, the love, and the mercy of God. I have to believe this was a promise of healing. The following week, the surgeon said this has been scirrhous cancer—it forms scar tissue. But there had been no scar in this picture! Each morning I wake up feeling excellent. It is a miracle that the Lord has given peace and joy to me. I do not dread each examination. I rather look forward to it. I know this is too soon to say medically that healing has taken place. But I have to believe by faith that it has. If I waver in this I am being faithless. Each day, Psalm 103:1 is precious, "and all that is within me," every cell of my body must praise Him: even undisciplined cancer cells must come under His discipline. And I can just thank the Lord and praise Him for allowing me to go through this experience! And there have been no more nightmares! Even my neighbors realize there is a new intensity in my life. I can sing while mowing the lawn, hanging out diapers, and pulling weeds!

I wonder if the sub-conscious mind registered the doctor's words during the first surgery that he thought perhaps there would be a year to live? Then the nightmares were an expression of trying to communicate and tell my husband. For in spite of good reports at first from the doctor, I felt the hopelessness of the case. Can this be possible?

Two instances of cancer of the breast have been noted in this chapter. In the first case the patient decided to rely strictly upon faith that she would be healed. Much valuable time was lost and despite the fact that surgical methods were finally resorted to, the patient succumbed to her illness. This is not to say that had she sought surgical attention immediately the outcome would have been different. However, with the methods which we have available today, the only chance for the patient with cancer of the breast, as far as science is concerned, is to get to the doctor as soon as any mass is found in the breast and not to procrastinate.

Those individuals who work either within the church or outside the church in the realm of the "healing ministry" should be extremely cautious in their advice to cancer patients. They should not advise against seeking early medical and surgical attention for cancerous disease. I believe implicitly in the Healing Ministry of the Church of Jesus Christ. However, I believe that this ministry should be used in conjunction with the best medical and surgical methods—not as a substitute for scientific methods. It is my belief that the answer to the prayer of the cancer sufferers often is the scalpel of the well-trained surgeon and those who work along with him aiming toward the total ablation of the cancerous growth.

The second patient whose letter is quoted sought medical attention early, but delay occurred as a result of a mistaken diagnosis. When surgical intervention was attempted the cancer had already spread beyond the confines of the surgical operation. The surgeon, as many surgeons are wont to do, decided to lie to his patient and tell her that the cancer had been removed despite the fact he had stated something differently at the time of the operation. He failed to realize that his statements in the operating room were made in the presence of his patient who registered them in her subconscious mind just as surely as if she had been awake. There then followed the series of events which she describes. Finally she sought the help of the Healing Church and miraculously she experienced first healing of her subconscious mind and her psychological problem which then was followed by physical healing.

What can be the differences in these two patients? Both believed in the healing virtue of Jesus Christ in His Church today. Both sought the help of the Healing Church. In both instances there was procrastination—one because the patient decided to wait of her own volition, and the other because of the reassurance of an erroneous diagnosis.

There are doubtless many factors in both cases we know nothing about, but there is one which occurs to me since I have seen more instances of the first type of patient than I like to think about. I do not believe that it is a manifestation of faith to neglect to seek help when it is available. Many people in this kind of situation substitute fear for faith. Actually, what they do is develop a morbid fear of their illness which paralyzes them from doing anything of a constructive nature with reference to their illness. They obtain some solace and some comfort from the healing ministry of the Church, but their fear remains, and their cancer with all of its roots in the subconscious mind continues to be present. Fear is perhaps the greatest ally of cancer and can only be removed from the person through an act of the will to do something about his illness and through the intervention of God in the total person of the individual—spirit, soul, and body. The Ministry of Healing should never be conducted apart from the doctor and the nurse, who, along with an enlightened clergy, should be the agencies

of the healing love of Jesus Christ toward cancer sufferers. This is admittedly an ideal which is rarely present in an area of scientific medicine which has ignored
the spiritual and been blind to the Healing Ministry.

The second case illustrates the profound need of the
enlightened physician for the Gospel of healing in the
medical profession today. Our lack of a spiritual approach produces a callousness and a cold impersonality
toward our desperate patients. Many seek help in the
terminal stages of illness from the fringe areas of medicine which can promise nothing but an even more
heartless using of the desperate patient and his family.

The course of the medically or surgically hopeless
case is of great concern to all thinking physicians who
are faced with the problem of cancer. Desperate attempts are often made by the patient or his family to
achieve a cure through the use of fringe-type cancer
treatments which are questionable or of no value. If the
concerned public and physicians were properly oriented
in this problem and better after-care methods were provided, false cancer-cure clinics which thrive on the mis-
fortune of dying people would soon disappear from the
public scene. There is a growing number of people beginning to realize that their place is at the doctor's side
in the effort to rid cancer from our lives. Some enlightened churches are holding healing services where the
patient can come for prayer and unction. The Healing
Church is a new phenomenon on the American scene,
and it is in this area that the physician as well as the patient sees an arm of support which has rarely been present before. It is to be sincerely hoped that through
prayer and through the confidence which comes to the
patient as a result of being surrounded by love and care,
and concern by a believing fellowship, that miraculous

things can occur. In every instance one should do everything medically and surgically possible to achieve healing from whatever disease condition he may have. Along with this, there should be concurrent prayer and the services of the enlightened Healing Church, such as the one in the quoted letter. When medical methods fail, the clergy must continue to uphold and uplift the patient. They can give him the constant support and optimistic viewpoint that—no matter what the situation—God has not failed; that there is always the possibility of spontaneous remission or cure of the disease. This can always be the possible outcome for the patient who does not despair but continues to trust God.

Even when the physician decides to incorporate the truth of Christian Healing into his practice, he is going to have apparent failures and disappointments. However, in those cases in which he does use this new philosophy of basic care, he will occasionally have cases in which results are spectacular and fascinating. This is not to say that the physician who adopts this philosophy will negate or diminish his scientific acumen. He adds to his scientific knowledge the necessary attributes of Christian belief and practice as recorded in the New Testament.

One such instance in my practice deserves mention. A middle-aged Jewish woman came to me for investigation of a mass in her right breast. She stated at the outset that the reason she had come to me was that I believed in prayer. Prior to the initial biopsy, the patient requested prayer. This gave the patient confidence and an inner sense of security prior to going to the operating room for what she realized might result in radical surgery. It also served to deepen the patient-doctor relationship. The mass proved to be cancer and the breast was radically removed. Within a period of several months, and during the time when the patient was receiving X-ray therapy, she developed signs of spread of the cancer to her mediastinum and to her right lung. An X-ray report from the radiologist who was administering therapy stated that there was metastasis to the right lung with neoplastic abscess, which contained a fluid level within it. During this time, the patient became progressively more ill.

She was re-hospitalized. Prior to the taking of additional X-ray studies, the patient again requested prayer. I recall going to her bedside one evening, taking her hand in mine, and praying for her. In the midst of the prayer, I asked Jesus to heal her. I realized at that instant that I had prayed in the name of Jesus and hesitated, feeling I had violated her religious belief only to feel her hand squeeze mine as if to say, "That's all right, go ahead!" I finished my prayer and much to my surprise the patient began immediately to improve. X-ray studies the following morning and additional studies the following week failed to disclose any residual neoplasm. The patient has continued well to this day. What caused the remission is difficult to say, except certainly it must be stated that the factors of faith and prayer were of paramount importance. Love and concern for the patient and a refusal to become discouraged in the face of a most alarming situation must play its part. The body and the soul do respond to the spirit, and particularly when the human spirit is in harmony with the Spirit of God.

And he said unto her, Daughter, be of good comfort: thy faith hath made thee whole Luke 8:48.

7 - Cancer II

THE PHYSICIAN who would consider Jesus Christ's message of healing must re-evaluate his entire approach to patient care in the light of the Gospel message if he would develop a Christian orientation toward God and his fellow man. When he does this, hopeless conditions suddenly do not appear as devoid of hope as they did before. Optimism replaces pessimism. As a Christ-oriented physician views man's mortal enemy, cancer, this is also true. Cancer is the continuing dilemma of modern medicine and surgery. It is a disease with many faces and disguises, making it treacherous and insidious in its development. Eventually it becomes a multi-disease entity which, as it progresses, involves physicians in many specialty groups. Physician and researcher alike today are looking for new therapies. The layman-patient is forced many times to his knees in prayer; so too, the doctor when so often he sees impending death despite all his methods and surgeries.

We live today in a world replete with many great advances which make the medical world of fifty years ago appear almost fictional, perhaps impossible. Surgical results in cancer are better today because of advances in medical treatment, surgical techniques, and medical technology; we better understand pathology and physiology. We have advanced in the fields of chemo-therapy and radiation treatment of cancer.

However, many modes of therapy are not curative but are at best only palliative or life-prolonging in their effect. It is wise, periodically, to view ourselves in the practice of medicine with a critical eye and hope that through wise criticism we may make progress and overcome complacency. Is there an assurance of hope in the individual cancer case which confronts us from day to day? In all honesty, it can be said that there is hope! There is also the chance that there may be no hope.

A patient who hears a physician's diagnosis of cancer has reached a tremendous and alarming crossroads in his life. The diagnosis of cancer may be categorized as a death sentence from which there is a possibility of reprieve. It is here that the physician and others caring for the patient must work together again to complete the care and to hold the patient up through the convalescent stages of his healing, or possibly through the terminal stages of the disease in the case of medical incurability. Even for the cured patient, the needed physical and psychological rehabilitation challenge the family, the doctor, and the clergyman. When the patient is medically incurable, the problem becomes much greater, and requires every resource of the physician's art, every ounce of love and understanding by the family, and prayerful support of the fellowship of the concerned in the Church.

Those interested in cancer patients must adopt a more personal interest in rehabilitation and the transformation of terminal care facilities to centers of healing. Cancer societies should do more than simply supply information, dressings, beds, or utensils. Facilities for the instruction of the patient's family and the home care of the patient should be provided. Consideration also should be given to methods of alleviating the huge financial burden placed upon the families in some cases where the disease is painfully slow in its course. Closer cooperation between cancer societies, medical societies, and the healing Christian church is an important and critical necessity.

In view of the cases cited herein, it becomes apparent that along with all present areas of investigation, cancer should be investigated from the standpoint of the spiritual. The development of many neoplastic diseases bespeaks evil.

Cancer is something which the body itself produces. It is not analogous to infection, an invasion of the body by an organism attacking the body from without. The cancer cell is a cell of the body itself which one day, as a result of some influence, begins to become self-asserting. That cell then develops an inclination to live for itself at the expense of the rest of the body. It creates its own colony of similar cells. These cells are sometimes large and often dark in their nuclear and mitotic appearance. Cancerous areas are rapid in their growth and vital in their rapidity of multiplication. Once having established themselves in a colony, the cells may invade blood vessels, on occasion, or lymphatic channels, and not only spread by direct continuity but send out emis-

saries to other parts of the body to colonize and repro-
duce. These cellular masses increase in size until either
the person who possesses such a disease is debilitated
by the rapidity of the growth, or vital organs become involved to the point where they cannot function and
death ensues.

The microscopic appearance of cancerous growth is
one of destructiveness and a selfish disregard for needs
of other cells which make up the harmony and function
of the body. The cells seem to have no realization that,
should they succeed in their purpose to take over, they
will ultimately cause the destruction of the body which
they inhabit to the point of destroying their own life in
the process. This, if it can be termed a philosophy, is
certainly the philosophy of the individual who decides
to live for himself and if necessary to destroy those
about him in order to achieve his own purposes. In
other words, the basic philosophy of cancer is what
might be termed that which has nothing to do with love,
but has to do with personal or selfish gratification. The
philosophy of cancer is satanic. If this is true, man must
not only investigate neoplasms from the standpoint of
the scientific and the surgical along with a multitude of
other avenues. The basic spiritual aspect of the disease
must be considered along with possible spiritual methods of its cure.

Not only does cancer have what seems to be a spiritual type of development, which is evil, but conceivably
it also could well have, because of its malignant nature,
evil etiological factors. Etiology means the knowledge
of causes of illness. It may be that in the background of
the individual developing cancer there is something
buried deep within the confines of the subconscious
mind of an emotional or spiritual nature such as hatred,

fear, hostility, disappointment, heartbreak, or a number of other factors. These emotions are every bit as much spiritual as they are psychological. When unresolved, they can lie smoldering within the depths of the subconscious mind, cropping out subsequently with the development of cancer, mental illness, or other conditions sometimes called "stress" diseases.

At one time during surgical training, I was privileged to be surgeon at a large prison. In the psychiatric unit of the prison was a young man who had become enamored of a girl whose family did not want to have him associated with their daughter. On one occasion, having left his work, he went to a bar to drink. After ingesting too much alcohol, he became angry and purchased a revolver. He then drove to his sweetheart's home and, drawing the gun, told the family that he was taking the girl with him. He took her in his car and drove off with her only to be found sometime later and arrested on the charge of kidnapping.

He was tried and convicted. In prison he became extremely quiet and progressively more unresponsive. Whenever anyone tried to help him, he would become angry and uncontrollable. Eventually, he was placed in the psychiatric division of the prison which, at that time, had rather primitive methods of dealing with such problems. About this time he began complaining of a physical difficulty and surgical consultation was obtained. This allowed me to see him. On examination, I found that he had a very large cancer of the lower bowel with involvement of the prostate and bladder, a situation which was entirely inoperable.

In his instance, we were confronted with the situation of cancer and the necessity of its surgical and medical management. However, there were serious psychological and spiritual factors which we never resolved because of our basic inability, in his instance, to see beyond the somatic problem. The physical problem became more and more acute as he was hospitalized over a period of months. Eventually he died. During this time, I was able to counsel with him on not only a psychological but a spiritual basis and was able to lead him to some measure of victory over his problem on the level of his spiritual being, as he became committed to Jesus Christ.

One wonders, in the development of his illness, had he sought spiritual counsel rather than going to a bar, and sought prayer and spiritual help in dealing with his sweetheart's family, if this entire process could not have been avoided. This is conjecture, but every physician who deals with cancer is confronted with similar problems which make him have concern that, perhaps on the level of the psychological and in particular the psychospiritual, we are missing a very important facet in the etiology and development of the disease cancer which should be more thoroughly investigated. Psychological studies have been carried out, but very little has been done in consideration of the spiritual. The error has been made in the past of considering the psychological and the spiritual to be the same. Not only should there be a consideration of the spiritual in the therapeutic and etiologic aspects of cancer, the entire problem should be subjected to deep spiritual consideration in all of its aspects.

Early in my surgical practice, I saw a young woman who had metastatic cancer of the breast. This young woman had the good fortune of being surrounded by a group of seriously concerned people in her church who were praying for her. I was asked to see her not from the surgical point of view but in order to give her spiritual support. Her physician was in accord with this approach, since there was no other avenue of help for her.

The point of interest in her case is that spiritual therapy, in this instance consisting of prayer, both with her and by church prayer groups without her, did indeed help her in the betterment of her physical and emotional status. In considering the development of her illness it is interesting to note she had deep psychological problems, not only with her family prior to her marriage, but a basic rebellion against her family and against all spiritual considerations.

She had married in an attitude of rebellion. Her marriage was an unhappy one in which she was never truly able to make a satisfactory adjustment. After development of her illness, during which the progress of the disease could not be stopped, her husband became concerned about her. When he started praying for her and loving her in a new and spiritually deeper way, she improved. Later however, her husband became interested in another woman; he stopped praying for her and being concerned for her, and the patient rapidly succumbed to her illness. The lack of love and replacement of love by resentment and indeed, hatred, are factors to be considered, not only etiologically but therapeutically, in cancer and any illness of man. Multiple studies have been carried out which demonstrate that animals and even plants surrounded by love and prayer will thrive, and those surrounded by hatred, resentment, argument, and similar factors, will wither.

In this day of scientific advances in which we are still striving so diligently to find the cause and treatment which will provide cure in the realm of cancer, it is well for the physician and the clergyman as well as the patient not to neglect the Gospel truth, that Jesus Christ is the Way and the Truth and the Life, and in Him lies hope, no matter how desperate one's situation may be.

It is unfortunate that cancer may be the factor which drives a person to his knees and to the necessity to seek the Lord in his life. But even this desperate aspect of the situation may not only save him unto eternal life; there is the distinct possibility that such a conversion may result in healing. Herein lies the realm which, in my opinion, should be investigated on a deeper level, not only by the church, but by those who are interested in the entire field of cancer and related diseases.

I am the way, the truth, and the life: no man cometh unto the Father, but by me John 14:6.

I am come that they might have life and that they might have it more abundantly John 10:10.

8 - The Infusion of Life

ONE OF THE most intriguing things about Christianity is its focus on life. A believer in Jesus Christ has not only the ground rules for abundant life on earth; he also sees how he may have eternal life. Eternal life is that life which the Christian individual lives now as he has come to Christ and accepted Him as Saviour. Eternity is a measure of time, pertaining to the future from the present instant on. Through Christ we are now living eternal life. "I write this to you who believe . . . in the name of the Son of God . . . so that you may know (with settled and absolute knowledge) that you [already] have life, yes, eternal life" (I John 5:13 *The Amplified Bible*).

If we are already living in our eternal life, then we must see that it is simply the mind and flesh which are temporal. The spiritual man continues on in the eternal sense. The body and the mind (the psychosoma) are the perishable aspects of our Adamic nature. "And so it is written, The first man Adam *was made* a living soul; the last Adam *was made* a quickening spirit." (I Corinthians 15:45). Any physician who has ever carried out an autopsy knows that the brain and the flesh are very much dead after respiration and circulation cease. It is perfectly obvious that something has departed from the individual which is most assuredly spirit. That peculiar glowing, life-like characteristic of the person is gone the instant death occurs. The ethereal spirit, the Christian believes, continues on to live forever with Christ. We know from the fact that Jesus was recognizable after his death and resurrection that we shall have, as St. Paul says, "an incorruptible body," that is to say a spiritual body which shall never see death or pain or disease, just as Jesus had.

This new creature (or creation) begins as soon as one has learned to begin dying to self and living unto Jesus Christ. This is the thrilling feature of Christianity. According to the Scripture, man does not enter into eternal nothingness nor does he live forever disembodied as an ethereal ghostly nebula. We shall, however, exist with our own bodies glorified and made more wondrously beautiful and functional.

It is most interesting to contemplate what Christ has made available to those who believe in Him. A person must stop thinking of his own possessions and of himself, and must take up his cross and follow the Lord Jesus Christ. He said man must be born again, "of the Spirit." If He is the Way, the Truth and the Life, we must truly believe this and begin to apply His way and His truth as well as His life in our life and practice.

For a doctor this becomes an important consideration, since doctors are in the life-conveying business.

When a baby is born, it is imperative that the mother's life be preserved and the infant's, as well. At times many hectic moments go by before the first infant cry is heard or, on occasion, before the mother is resuscitated. These are times when all physicians know that life is a very tenuous possession, capable of being snuffed out or lost at any instant.

The life of Christ, lived to the best of one's ability by the individual, can infuse life into the life and surroundings of the believer. Wherever Jesus went, He conveyed life. Wherever the believer in Christ goes, he conveys life. There are people so devoid of vitality that they everywhere convey only sorrow and depression. Such cannot be the characteristic of the believer in Christ. His very life and being should emulate the life and being of Christ. Since the Saviour and Healer of the world does indeed live and dwell within him, he must emulate Jesus as he lives out his personal "Imitation of Christ." He should be a conveyor of life in a very real way, just as Jesus was when He lived on earth, and just as He is as He dwells in the hearts of those who believe in Him.

There is an even deeper consideration, however, of the infusion of life than this. If the person who is interested in the Gospel of Jesus Christ reads the various narratives of the life of Christ with credulity, he must come to the conclusion that Jesus had a most striking ability when it came to dealing with those who were dead. One has no idea of how many instances there were in which Jesus raised the dead, but there are instances recorded in the New Testament which must be considered. It does not appear that Jesus ever gave a person mouth-to-mouth breathing or artificial respiration of any sort, nor did He carry out cardiac massage. Rather, the same method was used by Him as was used by God at the instant of the creation of the universe. God spoke the universe into existence, "And God said, let there be a firmament [the expanse of the sky] in the midst of the waters; and let it separate the waters [below] and the waters above" (Genesis 1:6 *The Amplified Bible*). Since God the Father spoke the universe and all of its contents into existence, it is not strange to see God incarnate, Jesus Christ, speaking life into the son of the widow of Nain, into Jairus' daughter, and into Lazarus.

The story of Lazarus is most important for the Christian to understand. I do not believe in demythologizing or diluting down the truth of the narrative in John 11. It is with reference to the raising of Lazarus that Jesus stated (John 11:25 *Amplified Bible*), "I am the Resurrection and the Life. Whoever believes in, adheres to, trusts in, and relies on Me, although he may die, yet he shall live. And whoever continues to live and believes— has faith in, cleaves to and relies on—Me shall never [actually] die at all. Do you believe this?" Immediately following this conversation, Jesus shouted with a loud voice, "Lazarus, come forth!" (John 11:43). The putrifying man who had been dead for four days came forth from his tomb wrapped in his burial garment!

This narrative can be taken allegorically or it can be believed realistically. As a physician, I prefer to accept the case history realistically even though it does not seem possible that anyone who is decaying and putrifying could be brought back to life. However, if Jesus is God incarnate, He has the capacity of giving life even unto death. If this be true, physicians need to know more about Christ since they, and all medical personnel, are interested in the preservation and bestowing of *life*.

In the emergency rooms of hospitals and in first aid

stations, on battle fronts, wherever emergency situations exist, the doctor and the nurse and those caring for the sick have the unusual sense, albeit at times rather a subconscious sense, of being involved in the area of the giving of life and even at times of the miraculous. There are those instances when one veritably despairs for the life of the person whom he is caring for, and in every physician's practice he has seen the moment of despair suddenly turn into the moment of hope. This may come as one plunges his hand into the chest cavity and begins to massage the heart and feels the flicker of life in his hand as the heart begins to assume its beat. There are those instances when the doctor, in order to reconvey life to an individual, may even break a bone or strike the chest of the patient, such an act creating such a reaction on the individual that life again resumes. I can remember an elderly Negro man who, at the moment anaesthesia began, suddenly developed a cardiac arrest. This was immediately ascertained. Anaesthesia was stopped and the patient was struck over the sternum forcibly with the fist. The heart immediately began beating and the patient was sent to the recovery unit without surgery being performed.

These are instances where a definite act is done upon the body, causing a recalling to life of someone who, to all intents and purposes, is dead or is very close to being so. The patient who has severely hemorrhaged, as in a ruptured tubal pregnancy or a bleeding ulcer or esophageal varices, who comes into the emergency room bled out, unconscious, and barely breathing, are examples where surgical treatment would almost appear miraculous. The physician, in such instances, will cut down upon a major vein and start the infusion of blood or plasma. Every physician has, under such circumstances, seen his patient go from imminent death to life.

The infusion of life which was done through Jesus Christ, as in the case of Lazarus, was something of a higher dimension. What makes this so vitally interesting to the person who will consider it, is the fact that Jesus stated, "Greater works than these shall he (the believer) do, because I go unto my Father" (John 14:12).

For the physician who finds himself in that critical moment of despair when everything seems to be lost, it is indeed a joyous and wonderful thing to contemplate that through Jesus Christ and through prayer in His name, despair may be turned into victory. Such a concept is hardly acceptable to the scientific mind since there are no formulae nor statistical bases upon which to establish such a consideration or hope. If man is a spiritual being, and life, on the eternal scale, is a characteristic which is imparted to man through Jesus Christ, the physician who is a conveyor of life and often the extension of the hands of Christ to the sick and suffering, must give more thorough consideration to the vital fact of what Jesus Christ can do for the physician himself.

There are a multitude of possible avenues of consideration, but two case histories come to mind in which the presence of the power of Jesus Christ spelled the difference between life and death. The author realizes that there is much room for discussion in both of the following cases, but insofar as is possible to determine, the factor spelling the difference between life and death, was the factor of belief in Jesus Christ, the presence of Jesus, and the power of His Holy Spirit in one's life and the imparting or infusing the life of Christ from one to another. Whatever a person is he manifests to others. If the individual is irascible and irritable with a sullen, angry nature, this personality will have its effect and will spread to everyone surrounding him. By contrast, if he is joyful and happy and looks on the light side of things, that individual will create about him an atmosphere of lightheartedness and pleasantness. Similarly, when a person is living the power of Jesus Christ in his life, the power of Jesus Christ must manifest itself in those whom he contacts. On a greater scale, when one is confronted with emergency situations such as death, if Jesus Christ is *Life,* He can be imparted through the believing Christian into the life of a person, even conceivably, one who has died.

On one occasion, when our youngest son was two, I was astounded one morning to walk into the bedroom and find that he had apparently expired during his sleep. I had checked him just a few moments before, and found him feverish, apparently from cold, but otherwise he seemed to be quite well. However, after the passage of a few minutes, on rechecking him, I found that he had no pulse and was not breathing. I can recall taking him into my arms and holding him up to God, and crying out, "Oh God, don't take my little boy from me!" I ran to the living room and, placing him across a footstool, I began to give him artificial respiration and to pray. After the passage of what seemed like an eternity in time, I felt him start to breathe and felt life come back into his little body beneath my hands. I took him immediately to the hospital and it was found that he had developed pneumonia, which condition cleared up without any residual difficulty within a few days.

In thinking about this wonderful healing and that God had privileged me to be a part of the healing of my son, I began to rationalize and felt that perhaps my son had just had an episode of apnea in which he had simply stopped breathing. It seemed that perhaps my personal concern and involvement with him could have been such that my clinical judgment was not as acute as it might otherwise have been. Perhaps I was unable to feel a pulse beat which actually was there. All these factors were coming into my mind as I attempted to reason it out. However, I could not deny the fact that, in response to my prayer, the Lord Jesus Christ had indeed given my little boy back to me and this I could not, on the level of my spirit, deny.

Some weeks later, making hospital rounds, I heard an announcement over the loudspeaker system calling for any doctor to come to the pediatric department immediately. Since it was mid-afternoon and no other physicians were present in the hospital, I went up and was asked by the nurse in charge to declare a little girl deceased. Out in the corridor a mother stood weeping. In the room, a resuscitator worked feverishly to send oxygen into the lungs of a two-year-old girl. I noted that the child was receiving intravenous fluids and noted that a powerful blood pressure stimulant was being given in the solution. I also noted that the oxygen tent in which the child had been placed was pushed aside and as far as could be determined, the child had died. There was no breathing discernible and when I placed the stethoscope upon her chest, I could not hear a heartbeat nor was the child breathing. This had been the condition for some minutes. At this point, I asked the nurse to go and get a cardiac stimulant which I intended to inject. After the nurse left the room, and prior to my saying anything to the mother, as I listened to the child's chest, I placed my hand upon her head and was led to pray, asking God who had given my little boy back to me, if he would give this little girl back to her mother. Such was my silent prayer. Before the nurse had returned to the room with the hypodermic, the child's heart had started to beat and she began to breathe. I went to the telephone and spoke to the pediatrician in charge of the case. His first question was whether or not I had secured permission for an autopsy. He told me the child had been seriously ill for several days with a terribly high temperature. Nothing that they had been able to do was able to resolve the condition. When he was told that the child was living, he gave the opinion that the child would not live, or if she did there would be something wrong with her mind. Nevertheless, the child did make an amazing recovery from that moment on.

There is something which we cannot define that God can give to those who believe in Him at times such as those which are quoted above. The light of Jesus Christ present within the inner man of the believer is such that it is transmissible to others even to the point of intervening in what otherwise might result in physical death. This same vital force transmitted into the life of the individual Christian is such that it can transform impossible situations into possible ones and darkness and hopelessness into light and optimism. This is a quality which life today needs desperately. The Gospel Truth needs to be taken from the Churches and from the pages of the New Testament and lived out in the lives of believers, particularly those who profess and call themselves Christians. Were those who profess Christianity to begin to believe it, and to live it, certainly the world would know it within twenty-four hours. "Jesus said unto her, I am the resurrection and the life; he that believeth in me, though he were dead, yet shall he live" (John 11:25). If the power of Jesus' resurrection is such, believers today should know what this power is. It should not be allowed to lie fallow in the institutional Church; it should be applied in the lives of those who are Christians. This is particularly true for those who are in the practice of medicine or nursing or surrounded with difficult and ofttimes impossible situations which in human terms are incurable or unimprovable. If Jesus Christ is God, and if His power is undiminished today, He who said that He would never leave us or forsake us, will be the factor in transforming the hopeless times of life into his Divine and glorious hope.

These things I have spoken unto you, that in Me ye might have peace. In the world ye shall have tribulation: but be of good cheer; I have overcome the world John 16:33.

"Fear not, little flock; for it is your Father's good pleasure to give you the kingdom" Luke 12:32.

9-Fear and Pain

How SHOULD man consider pain? How should he pray about it, either in himself or in others? Can it be wrong to want deliverance from it? How did the martyrs bear the ghastly tortures they were subjected to? Is there a difference between cancerous pain and martyrdom, the latter being voluntary in most cases? Is pain an enemy or a friend?

Since these vital questions recur frequently in a doctor's life and practice, they must be answered not only from a medical standpoint, but also from the aspect of the individual Christian. I have just come from a patient suffering severe pain from an abdominal neoplasm. As I have known her over a period of several years, both in health and in illness, it is necessary that I analyze her reaction to her disease and its pain. This patient has endured previous suffering at the time of major surgery and has been able to buoy herself up through faith in

God and through faith in her physicians. When she was in the hospital for surgery, she exhibited very little apprehension, tolerating hospitalization and after-care without difficulty. Recently, however, she developed new symptoms. Another operation was performed which revealed an inoperable malignancy within the abdomen. This time the patient exhibited post-operatively much more apprehension about her situation, especially when she was told, at her request, that it was impossible to remove the growth and that she would require radiation treatment. As a Roman Catholic, she received the Sacrament of Extreme Unction. She was advised as to the efficacy of prayer and the need always of relying on the love of God, who sends health and does not send disease. When these things were done, she improved greatly. As disease continues and pain becomes more a problem, I have observed in this patient's instance, as well as in others, that increasing apprehension and fear bring increasing pain. When I am with the patient, talking to her about faith and God's love and Christ's healing power, I have noted the patient's apprehension decrease; as she becomes calm, her pain lessens. God's perfect love casts out fear and as fear is cast out, pain also diminishes or becomes tolerable. In this particular connection, I have noted with Jewish patients and others who do not believe in Jesus Christ, that illness makes them conscious of the need for something greater than their own resources.

When one talks of the love of God and of the healing power of Christ, a wellspring of hope sends forth healing life into the weakening body. "Through the tender mercy of our God; Whereby the dayspring from on high hath visited us, To give light to them that sit in darkness and in the shadow of death, To guide our feet into the

way of peace" (Luke 1: 78-9). Jarring pain makes the
patient conscious of his body and of his own frailty.
Man likes to project himself into a realm outside of his
body many times, but pain acutely brings him back to
reality and makes him aware of the framework in which
our spirit and soul exist until death. The pain of medically hopeless illness so often brings the patient back to
the reality of his body that he tends to live completely
incarcerated by it, dwelling upon the physical abnormality in his body in every microscopic detail. This is
not only often the case in patients with physical disease,
but also in patients with neuroses.

When a hopeless situation is found, such as the patient I have described, it is necessary to instruct her on
the importance of her body. She must know how concerned God is for our bodies, since He created them.
Through the body, we are to reflect God's love, life, and
beauty. It is necessary that, as the patient is constantly
reminded of her body through pain, she accept its existence and the fact that she has something abnormal within the body which is causing pain. This is not to suggest
that the patient become resigned to pain or resigned to
illness, but the acceptance of the fact that the illness exists and that the body exists is important in its cure.
Then at this point, the patient can muster spiritual, psychological, and physical resources through prayer, the
prayers of the concerned, and through the ministrations
of the church. Healing can then occur even in hopeless
situations. I have noted in my practice that the patient
who is able to have spiritual therapy is enabled to rise
above his illness and its pain, although still living in a
sick body which he does not deny. When this is accom-
plished, the patient can get along with less medication,
or even with none. Herein lies the concept of body ob-

ject and body subject. Body object is the body with its illness as the primary and total consideration. Body subject is the body realized and accepted with its problems and illness, but as a part of a triune being—spirit, soul, and body able to respond in health even in the midst of pain and disease.

Pain becomes worse the more one fights against it. One must never become resigned to pain, but must accept the fact that God has created nerves which feel pain in order to protect us from injury or to inform us that something is at fault. When disease causes irritation of these same protective nerve endings, one should not curse God for giving us nerves that feel pain, but should realize that illness (which is not *of God*) is causing the problem. We then can take a step upward, knowing that God, who created our bodies, can give us strength and ability to overcome illness and pain. During childbirth, women find, as they accept the discomfort of labor contractions or "pains," if they can cooperate with their pains, using them to help deliver the baby, they will minimize the discomfort and shorten the time of childbirth.

It is not wrong to want deliverance from pain. No one wishes to suffer, whether it be from a toothache, a gallbladder attack, a surgically inoperable cancer, or martyrdom. In all instances where pain is a component, prayer and closeness to Christ should be a primary consideration. If the pain serves to bring one closer to Christ, he can then find that, even through this discomfort, he is turning what superficially may be thought to be a curse into a blessing. Thus the sufferer ascends to a higher level of consciousness, using the spiritualization of pain to be a stepping-stone toward God. The pain then does not become a stumbling block to the individual, but becomes a means of achieving greater spiritual heights. In the case of the toothache or the gallstone attack, the patient can seek and obtain surgical relief from the pain, athough a certain amount of suffering may be required in the curing. The individual's prayer life and prayer support of those who are helping, plus the spiritual ministrations of the church, will be of great help in bringing about rapid recovery. In the case of the inoperable cancer, the ideal treatment is prayer support, spiritual therapy, and loving medical and nursing care. This combination, added to personal prayer and belief, will serve to minimize pain.

With reference to martyrdom, usually only those who are unusually spiritual are subjected to martyrdom. It would not be martyrdom if one were not dying for faith and for belief. It is, therefore, possible for the person who faces martyrdom to rely heavily upon the strength which the indwelling Christ gives him through prayer. He can thus overcome the tortures inflicted upon him through the overcoming of the world through Jesus. The pain of illness can similarly be tolerated by the sufferer's inner faith in the overcoming power and love of Jesus Christ.

When one prays for the patient who is suffering with pain, he should visualize the patient as being completely whole, surrounded by the love of God, indwelt by the love of Jesus, and empowered by the strength of the Holy Spirit. He should lift those for whom he prays up to the healing light of Jesus. This lifts the sufferer above pain and above illness; it gives strength to the spiritual body and love which casts out fear and takes away anxiety, factors which increase pain. The prayer for the presence of Christ in us and about us, and in the patient and about the patient, is the prayer of power and will make the problem of pain less a problem and more indeed a blessing.

Fear, whether of death or illness, is a tool of Satan used to defeat Christians and to bring about all manner of illnesses and emotional problems. Fear activates disease process as well as symptoms. The Holy Bible states, "There is no fear in love; but perfect love casteth out fear: because fear hath torment" (1 John 4:18). God is love, and therefore where God is there can be no fear, and where fear is there can be no God. Mathematically, this would be called an inverse proportion. The more fear we have, the less of God we have; the more of God we have, the less fear we have. Paul states in Romans 8:15, "For ye have not received the spirit of bondage again to fear; but ye have received the Spirit of adoption, whereby we cry, 'Abba, Father.' " Before one can receive the indwelling of the Holy Spirit, he must lay down his self, his intellectual being, as well as his ideas and traditions. Under these circumstances, one full of the Holy Spirit becomes convinced of the reality of Jesus Christ and His Resurrection Life. When this occurs, death is seen as something which has no sting, and the grave is seen as something which has no victory. Then the individual can state, as a French doctor friend of Tournier's did at the time of his impending death, when his physician wanted to give him medication to take away his pain, "Do not give me anything; I will not have anyone steal my death away from me."

We also need to recall the statement of Isaiah 4:5, "And the Lord will create upon every dwelling place of Mount Zion, and upon her assemblies, a cloud and smoke by day, and the shining of a flaming fire by night: for upon all the glory *shall be* a defence." I sincerely believe that the glory of the Lord in the total being of the Christian is a defense not only against evil but also against disease and fear. If God protects the believer from illness, from poisons, from serpents, (Mark 16:17-18), why then should he fear?

A physician might paraphrase Job 33:19-26 in the following way: "Man is chastened with pain upon his bed and all of his bones ache with heavy pain so that he may not desire food and is even revolted by it and his flesh shrinks away and his bones stick out. Such a man in his illness perceives his soul to be drawing near the grave and his life is ebbing away. If there were a minister, a pastor, or one person in a thousand to show this man the way of uprightness and lead him to the Way, then God is gracious unto him and says, 'Preserve him from death, for the ransom has been paid on Calvary's Cross.' Then shall his flesh become fresher than a child's and he shall return in strength to the days of his youth. Then shall he pray unto God and God will show him favor. He shall look upon his countenance with happiness and his new righteousness within will he give forth unto his fellow man."

The same God through the same Jesus is the same today, as He was in the yesterday of Job, or the yesterday of the man with the withered arm, or the man who sat crippled, begging for bread at the gate called Beautiful. When should the Christian ever fear? Fear, death, sin, and illness were defeated at Calvary. Through belief in Jesus Christ, man is given peace and the ability to make his body subject, not the object, of his total being. When, through faith, he has learned this truth, one who believes can live above fear and pain even in the face of cancer or martyrdom.

And the Lord God caused a deep sleep to fall upon Adam, and he slept; and he took one of his ribs, and closed up the flesh instead thereof Genesis 2:21.

10-The Challenge of Unconsciousness

ON OCCASION there will enter into the practice of the physician or into the hospital, a patient who is unconscious or comatose. The immediate problem of unconsciousness, or coma, is of great interest to the physician. The patient in diabetic coma is a tremendous challenge to the internist. In the event that the patient has pathology in the central nervous system, the neurologist and the neuro-surgeon diligently seek the cause of the problem and its proper treatment. As in all comparable situations, the acute problem is of much more interest to the physician than the chronic one. If it is impossible for the patient to be returned to consciousness, either through medical management or through surgery, he enters the category of chronicity in which both the medical staff and the nursing staff may give progressively less attention to his needs beyond the barest necessities. Such patients are often called "vegetables." Nursing care is directed toward the physical needs of the patient so that bed sores do not develop, and normal respiratory exchange is maintained. Since there is no possibility of questioning the patient to determine his needs and desires, this type of patient becomes uninteresting and peripheral to the main stream of both medical and nursing care.

Of similar challenge and interest is the patient who is unconscious as the result of anaesthesia. Such a patient is like the patient who is unconscious for medical reasons whether it be an overdose of sleeping pills or a cerebrovascular accident. Under anaesthesia, the narcotized cerebral cortex inhibits the patient's ability to cerebrate. With the body insensitive and unable to react except in a vegetative way, the surgeon can then proceed with the operation which is planned to correct a physical abnormality. With the patient unable to feel or respond, and with surgeon and the anaesthesiologist concentrating on factors of the operation, it is amazingly possible to give attention so much to the procedure at hand that the patient as a whole is forgotten. Thus, during the operation, as the technical procedure goes ahead, it may be the case that the surgeon will discuss the entire realm of anatomy, pathology, and surgery in general of the condition upon which he is operating. He may quiz his internes or residents. On finding the abnormal process, he may describe it minutely, offering audibly opinions to those in the operating room concerning prognosis of the condition. To a certain extent, all of this is understandable and reasonable.

There are situations which may not be as academic and enlightened as the instance cited. As the operation proceeds and things go well, there may be discussion of philosophy, sports, politics, or daily events without any regard for the fact that the patient is lying there asleep and conceivably, on the level of his spiritual being, able to absorb much of what is going on. If the surgeon is one who is vulgar or profane, it may be that the patient and observers are subjected to profanity or off-color stories. One of the great disappointments of surgery for me was to find that the operating room was not a sacred place; rather it was very much a workshop, at times devoid of true respect, particularly toward the individual who was anaesthetized. It was amazing to me, as a young surgeon, to note the difference between the types of conversation carried on in the operating room when the patient was awake, as under spinal anaesthesia, and when he was asleep under general anaesthesia.

I once visited a large city where much surgery is done on the heart and major blood vessels. I elected to go to one of the hospitals to observe a heart operation. The patient was a little boy. During the early stages of the operation, the boy was already under anaesthesia and as the cardiac bypass system was put in place, I noted with dismay that music piped into the operating room was anything but calm. I felt that music piped into an operating room would be most salutory for patient and those who work in the operating room, particularly in such an operating room where there is great tension and much detail to be considered. However, this operating room was filled with frenetic, upsetting music. Coupled with conversation and the technical procedure, it created an atmosphere of bedlam rather than the peace and quiet which should be the atmosphere of an operating room. I noted that, when the surgeon got to the part of the operation in which the heart defect was to be repaired, he had the music turned off. Things at that time became quiet. Following the closure of the heart and the conclusion of the surgery, the operating room again became filled with conversation and noise. It was distracting to those observing the procedure and certainly must have been to everyone, especially the little patient, if only on the level of his subconscious or his spirit.

Another time I met a young woman victim of a cerebrovascular accident. She had been suddenly seized with a severe headache; within a few minutes she had lapsed into unconsciousness. She was sped to a local hospital where a neuro-surgeon was summoned. In the operating room openings had been drilled into her skull, a hemorrhage identified, and the hemorrhage pressure relieved. Following this procedure and a period of critical illness, the patient was left with a paralysis of half her body and an inability to say what she was thinking. Also, she noted from the time she began to be aware after the stroke, she had a constant whirring sensation in her head.

At the time I met the patient, she had been ill more than two years. She attended a lecture I gave, in which I discussed my feeling that statements made in the presence of sleeping children, or of those anaesthetized, were capable of creating problems subsequently in those who heard such conversations, albeit on the spiritual or subconscious level. She suddenly became aware that she remembered some of the things which had been said while she was unconscious during the surgery. For one thing, she remembered the sound of the drill as it penetrated her skull; she also remembered some of the conversation between surgeon and nurse. She recalled, for example, that the nurse had made a derogatory comment about her which, even in her state of unconsciousness, created an extreme feeling of resentment. When this fact came to the point of being recognized, she asked God to forgive her for her resentment and to wash away all of the effects of this resentment from her being. To her amazement, she immediately was released of anxiety and concern, and most amazing of all, the whirring sensation in her bead suddenly disappeared, never to recur!

In the letter quoted from the patient with breast cancer, her surgeon had told her that the cancer had been completely eradicated by surgery. She said that she was extremely shattered some months later, when her surgeon told her that her situation was hopeless. She had previously been told that all the malignancy had been removed. She found, in conversation with friends, that the surgeon during the operation had stated that the situation was serious when he found not only the growth present in her breast, but spread into the lymph nodes of the axilla. Post-operatively, the patient experienced continuing apprehension and what she described as nightmares. No doubt the apprehension, the ill-defined fears, and the uncertainty which she experienced post-operatively were related to the imprinting of the negatives stated in the operating room upon the patient's subconscious mind and upon her spirit at the time of the surgery.

There was a time when I was asked to see a child who had sustained a cardiac arrest approximately three months previous. This young girl had been unconscious and was living in a state of vegetation ever since the cardiac arrest and the time of being resuscitated. At the time of my examination, there was not a glimmer of consciousness. She lay thrashing about in her bed and looked very much like one trying to tear out of an envelope of darkness. She had a tracheotomy tube in her throat, a feeding tube in her stomach, and a catheter in the bladder. She was emaciated and severely, chronically, and terminally ill. Everything concerning her was despair. No hope was given to her or to her parents by the attending staff of the hospital. So far as could be determined the child had only a very short time in which to live.

In view of some of my convictions concerning the ability to affect the spiritual being through conversation and prayer, it was my recommendation to the parents, to the nurses, and to attendants that nothing negative be further said in the presence of the patient. I felt there should be no prognostication over the patient, but that everything that was to be said should be in the optimistic. I encouraged the mother to visit the child frequently, to pray audibly with her, and to state such things as, "Karen, Jesus is healing you and you are going to become well." Besides the audible expressions of optimism, it was my feeling that the parents and those visiting the child should actually change their attitude toward her and begin to feel that she was not going to die, but that she was going to get well. In this context, they were encouraged that where Jesus Christ is, there is life and hope, and that as they believed in Jesus, nothing would be impossible. They were also encouraged to say those things which were familiar to their daughter so that old patterns of thought and action could be brought to mind. With this change in attitude and approach, it was not very long before the child started to come out of her coma and began to recover.

When I visited Dr. Paul Tournier in Geneva, a member of the Bossey Medical Group was asked his opinion concerning prayer with the patient. After giving the matter some thought, he stated that he believed in prayer, but he also believed in helpful and health-giving attitudes on the part of nurse and physician. For example, he stated that in his practice many patients were given shock therapy for their mental conditions. He said, "Every bit as important as voiced prayer, if not more important, is what kind of eyes are going to greet the patient when he awakens from his shock therapy? Are they the eyes of love and care and concern or are they cold and impersonal?" Similarly, it might be asked, what kind of hands and arms care for and lift the patient from the treatment table to the stretcher and into his bed? What kind of an atmosphere of love and regard is there surrounding those people who care for the patient?

It is my considered opinion, after the observation of many anaesthetized patients, that it is possible to implant negatives into the subconscious mind and conceivably into the spiritual being of the patient at the time of anaesthesia or unconsciousness which are of definite bearing on the patient's post-operative course and on the total outcome of whatever procedure has been used to correct his abnormality. Every bit as important as the technical aspects of the procedure are those factors which occur about the patient during the time of his unconsciousness. In this regard, it might be also stated that in one's home, one must never think that his children or any sleeping person is unable to receive and know spiritually what is going on during the time of sleep.

There are many situations, not only in the home, but especially in the hospital, where it is entirely possible for the patient to be adversely affected by those things which occur while he is not conscious. Therefore, consideration should be given to post-anaesthesia recovery rooms. Every effort should be made to make such areas as orderly and quiet as possible. Greater attention should be placed upon protecting the delicate sensibilities of the patient, particularly the patient who is unconscious. Conversations and noisiness in such a situation should be absolutely minimal. In this situation, as in the operating room, the use of quiet background music could conceivably be beneficial. Similarly, attention should be given to intensive care units which also are places in which the comatose patient may be placed. Again, in these areas, there is apt to be noise and confusion, plus the frenzy and scurrying about which are so common in places where life hangs in the balance. It is so easy in medicine and in nursing to be imbued with the problems at hand to the point where the patient's individual needs are pushed aside in order to take care of simply the major and critical considerations. In all such situations, as in the operating room, honor must be paid to the patient as an individual and as a human being. That honor must never be neglected, either as a result of expediency or neglect.

A friend of mine is a very deep-thinking psychiatrist. He has given considerable attention to spiritual factors in medicine, particularly psychiatry. At one time he was discussing the fact that a patient who is asleep or unconscious is able to know what is happening about him. Ministers, he said in his lecture, should not be upset when parishioners fall asleep during sermons. Under such circumstances, he said, the message gets through to the mind unimpeded by extraneous factors such as sight, hearing, or wandering thought. This type of thinking has been utilized through what has been called "sleep therapy." Certain positive thoughts are transcribed on tape recorders and played during the night beneath the pillow of the sleeping patient. Music has been similarly used to calm sleeping patients by using tape recorders to increase the calmness of sleep. It is interesting, also, to consider hypnosis and the fact that a susceptible subject will demonstrate he has received certain positive facts which he carries out in the post-hypnotic state.

It is entirely possible that certain positive or negative verbal suggestions which are given to the patient under anaesthesia or sleep may similarly affect the person in terms of agitation or delay of post-operative recovery. Negative suggestions or statements, therefore, should be eliminated from operating rooms and from post-anaesthesia recovery rooms in the same way as they are not allowed in areas where a patient might hear them.

From the positive point of view, it is possible that if the patient is told that everything went well during the operation and that he will make a wonderful recovery and will awake feeling well,—that such suggestions could not help but ameliorate the patient's post-operative course.

I have found, in my own practice, where I am able to keep operating room conversation down to a minimum and allow only positive statements to be made over the patient during the operation and following the operation, the patient does considerably better. I have found, in this regard, that when an operation is started with audible prayer, that such an act creates a more salutary atmosphere in the operating room and positively stops peripheral conversation, particularly with reference to things which do not pertain to the operation itself.

By contrast, if an operation is not started with prayer and if the operating room team is not oriented to God in some positive way, very often the operating room can become a place where there is much negative conversation and discussion of many topics irrelevant to the case. I should like to suggest that every doctor who professes himself a Christian follow the precept established by Ephraim McDowell, the first American surgeon to ever perform a laparotomy; Dr. McDowell began his first operative procedure with prayer. Similarly, Dr. Hugh Kelly, of Johns Hopkins Medical School, always preceded his operative procedures with prayer. There is no more deeply spiritual discipline which the surgeon can utilize before operating. The prayer carries with it an absolutely positive suggestion for good and for benefit, not only to the patient but to members of the operating team. Following the operation, the patient should have the positive suggestion given to him that all has gone well, that God has answered prayer, that he has been protected through the operation, and that he is going to get well.

Investigations of twilight sleep have demonstrated that the patient can be interrogated under minimum degrees of anaesthesia and suppressed thoughts and feelings of the subconscious can be ventilated. If such ventilation is possible at this point, it is conceivably true that positive suggestions can likewise be implanted into the patient who is emerging from and entering into anaesthesia.

Certain specific instances are worthy of mention at this point. A prominent minister's wife went into the hospital for the delivery of a first infant. Shortly after arriving in the hospital, she began to hemorrhage and it was necessary for her to be taken immediately to the operating room where an emergency Caesarian section was carried out, during which procedure the patient was given blood transfusions in order to bring her out of shock. Not only was the patient in shock when she went into the operating room, but an anaesthetic was administered. Following the operation the patient was able to describe to the operating surgeon every detail of the procedure and much of the conversation in the operating room. Not only was there auditory memory, but she described the delivery of the infant, the fact that the surgeon had blood on the front of his operating gown, and many other factors. This latter fact is strange because a screen was placed between the patient and the operating team. So it was impossible for the patient to have seen the operation except by witnessing the procedure spiritually rather than psychologically. It can be theorized that the patient was under very light anaesthesia, but insofar as could be determined by the patient's husband, and by the patient herself as she recalled the incident, she was in shock when she went into the operating room and was anaesthetized with general anaesthesia.

In the *Journal of the American Medical Association* there was an interesting article from this standpoint. The authors described the case of a forty-year-old woman who was having a surgical operation for the correction of a cystocele and rectocele. The operation lasted two hours and fifty minutes and the anaesthesia time was three hours and ten minutes. A general anaesthetic was used along with the administration of neuro-muscular blockade. The authors comment, "Despite this apparently uneventful anaesthetic, the patient had a most unpleasant experience to relate to the surgeon and the anaesthesiologist. She had been intermittently conscious and unconscious during the three hour anaesthetic period. She volunteered the information that an airway had been inserted in her mouth and removed at some later time. She reconstructed details pertaining to the dis-

cussion of the blood loss and the decision to start administration of the second unit of blood. She also experienced dull, unbearable, pelvic, lower back, and perineal
pain during much of the operation."

It is thus apparent that, even in cases albeit rare in
occurrence, some patients are going to be aware of what
is happening in the operating room. Even were the surgeon and the anaesthesiologist to ignore the possibility
of deleterious influence on the patient because of conversations in the operating room being picked up by the
patient's spirit or subconscious mind, there is always the
real possibility that such a case as the one described
may occur and that the patient may indeed not only be
hearing much of what is going on but may even be feeling what is being done.

An interesting comment is made by J. F. Artusio,
writing in the *Journal of the American Medical Association*. "Quite by accident, one of my patients (under a
light plane of anaesthesia) responded to the spoken
voice and indicated freedom from pain." Based upon
this observation, Dr. Artusio taught a method of giving
anaesthetics in which the patient was carried along on
very light anaesthesia which he determined to be suffi-
cient to knock out the pain sensation, but still of such a
shallowness of anaesthesia that he was able to converse
with the patient and determine whether he was feeling
pain or discomfort and in general, able to determine the
patient's verbal and cerebral responses to the operative
procedure.

These instances are cited primarily to serve as a basis
of deeper consideration of the effects of unconsciousness, whether it be the operating room or a situation in which the patient is in coma. Anyone who is
asleep or comatose must be treated as if he were awake

and able to comprehend. Nothing negative should be said around him. If it is at all possible, spiritual factors should be considered such as prayer, and positive suggestions relative to the patient's recovery and his state in general should be given on the part of medical and nursing attendants. Under such circumstances, it cannot help but be of positive benefit to the patient and to everyone concerned, as the tenor of the operating room and the tenor of the sick room in general respond to a higher orientation of doctor and nurse toward the human being whom they are treating and toward God who must truly be considered primary in all medical and nursing situations.

And one of the scribes came, and having heard them reasoning together, and perceiving that he had answered them well, asked him, Which is the first commandment of all?

And Jesus answered him, The first of all the commandments is, Hear, O Israel; The Lord our God is one Lord; And thou shalt love the Lord thy God with all thy heart, and with all thy soul, and with all thy mind, and with all thy strength: this is the first commandment Mark 12:28-29-30.

. . . Holy Father, keep through thine own name those whom thou hast given me, that they may be one, as we are John 17:11

11-Synthesis

IN MEDICINE today, as in theology, there is a tendency to divide man into a number of different categories. Those interested in theology concentrate upon man's spiritual being and those factors which relate to his spiritual being. This may be seen even in the sociological consideration, which is apt to be theoretical and ethereal. The minister who would leave his church to march in a parade, carrying a sign for some sociological objective, may do so more in an effort to identify with, rather than to actually be a part of the group which he represents. He remains isolated from the real problem no matter how idealistic his desire may be. Similarly, in psychiatry, the psychiatrist lives and practices in a realm relatively isolated from medicine in general. Psychiatry as a field is also isolated by and large from theology. Insofar as medicine itself is concerned, instead of being one science concerning the body, it has been fragmented into various specialty fields. What is needed is a SYNTHESIS, or bringing together, of all the various concepts of man. Fragmentation destroys, whereas synthesis creates. It is necessary that man the human being be studied and treated from the standpoint of his whole being rather than in a piecemeal and incomplete manner.

Fragmentation medicine is not in the best interest of the patient. Many examples could be cited. Recently I was asked to see a patient in the southwest who was critically ill with cancer. When this man had first become ill, I was contacted by telephone. I had recommended a surgeon located near the patient. Shortly after the patient arrived in the hospital, the recommended surgeon told my patient that he was about to vacation in Europe, and since the patient had certain urological problems, he was going to call in a urologist. The urologist, an excellent man in his field, did not see that patient except from his specialty standpoint. Unfortunately, before the surgeon could return from Europe, the surgical condition, which had not been the matter of primary concern, had created such severe problems that the patient had become critically ill. At this point, I was called upon to go and see him. After examining the patient, I talked at length with his wife. She made the comment that, in discussing her husband's condition with the urologist, she had been told that the only aspect of her husband which he was qualified to answer questions about, or to take care of, was his urological system, and that she would have to talk to someone else regarding the surgical problem. Herein lies the great problem of specialty medicine which grows greater as medicine becomes even more scientific. The patient becomes lost in the morass.

Fragmentation is altogether too common in medicine today. To counteract this problem, in some medical centers after a patient has been studied diagnostically, he is brought back to the original physician who takes all the consultation reports and laboratory studies and puts them together. Then he gives the patient and his family a complete picture of what is wrong. Too often, however, in specialty type situations, the patient is left confused, fragmented, and uncertain as to what is wrong with him. Beyond this fragmentation, there is a relative lack of consideration on the part of medicine in general to the psychological factor. Most physicians today think to only a minor extent about the psychiatric realm. They prescribe tranquilizers frequently and consider many of their patients to have nervous problems. Insofar as any true type of psychotherapy or attempt to get at the primary psychiatric problem is concerned (if this is the trigger mechanism of the patient's disease), this is rarely done. This attitude may be an outgrowth of the increased busyness of practice or it may simply be a desire not to be concerned about anything other than the immediate physical problem which presents itself. Certainly, caring for the immediate problem carries with it less necessity for the physician to identify with the patient or to become involved with him on any more than a superficial level.

Beyond the basic neglect of the psychological in medicine is neglect and disregard of the spiritual. In World War II, it was common for physicians to seek the chaplain's help in critical situations. This has become less and less apparent since the end of the war. Altogether too often the patient, as well as the physician, may not consider the spiritual except in those instances when death appears imminent. This is extremely unfortunate. A physician not oriented toward the spiritual who suggests a visit with the chaplain or perhaps even suggests that he himself pray with the patient may make the patient feel that his illness is more severe than he had thought, perhaps that he is about to expire.

A new and enlightened type of medical practice is needed in which the physician, even though a specialist, truly identifies on a deeper level with his patient and sees him as a whole individual. He must see that even something which involves the tip of the toe may, in its pain, its eventual consequences, involve the entire body. There is nothing that happens to any part of the envelope in which we live which can affect us only in an isolated area. We are aware that there are not only neurological factors which are involved whenever portions of the body are subjected to trauma or disease, but there are also hormonal and enzymatic considerations, lymphatic and circulatory aspects, as well as psychological and spiritual factors which cannot be neglected or ignored.

The urgent need, then, is synthesis! The physician must work in greater cooperation with the psychiatrist. Both the physician and the psychiatrist must see the clergyman in a new light as an ally and not someone simply to be called in for last rites, a prayer, or reassurance prior to death. Even as committees on religion and medicine are established in medical societies and in seminaries and psychiatric hospitals, the appointment of committees does not constitute a true answer to the dilemma of fragmented man. Unfortunately, there has not even been an adequate attempt to understand psychosomatic medicine. The psychiatrist is altogether too infrequently consulted concerning the patient with organic illness. He is rarely called to give strength and solace to the dying. Perhaps the reason for this is a basic feeling that the psychiatrist has become devoid of true consideration of the spiritual. The person who has centered his life in God and in Jesus Christ may fear that the psychiatrist may consider a vital orientation toward Christ equivalent to mental illness. A common concept in psychiatry is that troubled man turns to alcohol, sex, or religion for his solace. Religion is seen as a means of escape from reality. Religion is viewed warily and the spiritual aspect of man is rarely considered. Perhaps some of the reason for this is the fact that theologians have tended to go towards psychiatry rather than the psychiarist going towards religion. Many ministers have established psychological counseling centers in relationship with their churches, but these efforts have been primarily on the level of the psychological, often with the orientation toward Freudian psychiatry rather than any absolute or even tenuous relationship toward Jesus Christ. In the synthesis of man, there is a necessity for the minister or the theologian to re-orient man toward Jesus Christ. In their ministration to the patient, they should not attempt to practice psychiatry or a form of religious psychiatry. They should practice logotherapy—the treatment of the spirit of man who can only be made whole through finding a meaning in life, such as provided by vital contact with Jesus Christ. To answer the anxieties and neuroses which plague intellectual man today, the psychiatrist must see that beyond the psychiatric is the spiritual; as he presents the psychiatric answer to the problem, he is only presenting a portion of the answer. The physician must see that he must not ignore the psychological and spiritual factors as he undertakes to always create a well patient. To be well is to be whole!

In Switzerland, conversing with Dr. Paul Tournier

and Professor Karlfried Graf Von Dürckheim, I once asked Dr. Tournier if successful healing after prayer were not something originating on the spiritual level and through the spiritual experience, as the mind, convinced healing had occurred, effected a body response in becoming well. Both Dr. Tournier and Dr. Von Dürckheim felt that the healing came through prayer, the spiritual being was healed through coming into harmony with God. The body was then healed as it responded to the spirit.

Then Von Dürckheim said, "The mind becomes healed as it, like a jealous little boy, lingers behind and waits to see what is happening, doubting and questioning whether healing can possibly have occurred." The mental area is the doubting, the questioning, and the worrying part of man. It is, therefore, necessary for us to realize that there is a spiritual being, and that this spiritual being contacting God through Jesus Christ and the indwelling Holy Spirit, is able to overcome the mental nature of man and make the body whole. In the process, the mind is also made well.

It is interesting to read in the New Testament that Jesus always approached man as a primary spiritual consideration. Also, He did not heal man in the ordinary sense. To the woman with the "bloody issue" (Mark 5), He did not say, "Your physical problem has been healed," but He did say, "Thy faith hath made thee *whole*" (Luke 8:48). In the story of the man who was born blind, the narrative does not deal with a man who has simply had his vision restored, but with a man who developed a deep spiritual belief in Jesus Christ, and who, despite the pressures of society and the negative attributes of those about him, decided to follow Jesus no matter what the consequences. It was more than just simply a return of sight, but it was a manifestation of a total healing on all levels of his being. Many New Testament examples could be cited where the ministry of Jesus Christ was not simply that of the physician curing a specific illness, but was presenting the Kingdom of Heaven to man. He gave encouragement to man: not only could he be healed of disease, but he could become *whole* in spirit, soul, and body, as he became a new person through Jesus Christ.

The synthesis required in the New Medicine is one which can come about through the avenue of a deep and real consideration on the part of a physician, ministers, psychiatrists, and man. They all must consider the place of the Lord Jesus Christ in life today. Jesus is the Synthesizer! He is the One who first showed how man can be brought together, rather than fragmented. It is wonderful to be able to treat physical illness with today's drugs and medications and operations. It is tragic, however, that so often we end up with a broken vessel. Psychiatry does not always put this broken vessel back together again. Psychiatry may teach a person how to live as a broken vessel, but Jesus, through awakening the spiritual and making a new creation of man, renews the psychological being and renews the physical being in the process! "Be not conformed to this world: but be ye transformed by the renewing of your mind . . ." (Romans 12:2). This statement indicates that it is possible for an absolute renewal of the mental nature of man. This statement does not indicate the necessity for tranquilizers, or shock therapy, or psychotherapy, but does indicate that through Jesus Christ and coming apart from the world into the Kingdom of Heaven which Jesus talked about, man can have a transformation of his mental being. Along with this there is the absolute fact that man, as he comes to Jesus Christ in the Kingdom of Heaven, can have a transformation of his physical being. This evolves as the spiritual being, the inward man, quickens to life through Jesus Christ.

The spiritual being exists as a small atrophic seed in man until it is nourished by the waters of the Holy Spirit. If the seed is fed by the forces of evil through immorality and the breaking of the Commandments of God, the inward man may develop as distorted, grotesque, and productive of sickness. On the other hand, if the spiritual seed is nourished by God through conversion, reading of the Bible and through concentration of the person upon those things which are good, he develops in the Godly direction and becomes what the New Testament calls a new creature. St. Paul said it this way, "It is sown a natural (physical) body; it is raised a supernatural (a spiritual) body. [As surely as] there is a physical body, there is also a spiritual body" (I Corinthians 15:44 *The Amplified Bible*). The spiritual body is not something which appears at the moment of death to go on to live with God forever if we have followed the precepts of God in our lives and not violated the Commandments. The spiritual body begins to live as soon as man realizes that his potential is that of being triune, (logo-psychosomatic) through Jesus Christ, rather than biune (psychosomatic) without Him. St. John, in his first Epistle, said, "It doth not yet appear what we shall be: but we know that, when he shall appear, we shall be like him; . . ." (I John 3:2). In this consideration, it can be seen that God, as He is portrayed in the Bible, is triune. That is to say that He has three natures: that of God the Father (the Creator and Organizer of the universe, "Elohim"), the Son (the manifestation of God in the form of man), and Holy

Spirit (the spiritual essence of God and of Jesus Christ existing potentially in man since Pentecost and existing in the world prior to Jesus Christ as an occasional gift to certain prophets and seers). Likewise, man has the potential of being three in one. The spiritual aspect does not come into existence until he is "born again," not physically, this time, but spiritually. The psychosomatic man, who has not been "born of the spirit," is a partial man and potentially a sick man, carrying within him the seeds of sickness and death. Triune man (the logo-psychosomatic man) would fulfill the category spoken of by St. John, "When He shall appear, we shall be *like* Him," three in one.

The New Testament writings of St. Paul are replete with this type of consideration. St. Paul, having had an absolute revelation of Jesus Christ in his life, was able to see this relationship of man in both its partial or psychosomatic considerations, and its whole or logo-psychosomatic ideal. Writing in Romans 12:1, St. Paul says as he regards the body, "I appeal to you, therefore, brethren, and beg of you in view of [all] the mercies of God, to make a decisive dedication of your bodies—presenting all of your members and faculties—as a living sacrifice, holy (devoted, consecrated) and well pleasing to God, which is your reasonable . . . and spiritual worship." He states further (Romans 7:23-25), "I discern in my bodily members—in the sensitive appetites and wills of the flesh—a different law (rule of action) at war against the law of my mind (my reason) and making me a prisoner to the law of sin that dwells in my bodily organs. . . . O unhappy and pitiable and wretched man that I am! Who will release and deliver me from [the shackles of] this body of death? O thank God!—He will! through Jesus Christ, . . . our Lord! So

then indeed I of myself with the mind and heart serve
the Law of God, but with the flesh the law of sin." In
the following chapter, St. Paul gives the answer in that
he speaks of the spiritual aspect of man and identifies
the "mind of the flesh" as the mind of man without the
Holy Spirit. The mind of man without the Holy Spirit is
identified as the mind of the flesh which is death. In Romans 12, St. Paul beseeches that man be transformed
(*not* transform himself) by the renewing of the mind.
"Let this . . . mind be in you which was in Christ Jesus"
(Philippians 2:5). Psychosomatic man is described in
Romans 7 and the fulfillment of man showing how man
can be whole through the indwelling of the Holy Spirit
and the coming-alive and growth within man of his spiritual being is described by St. Paul in Romans 8. (*The
Amplified Bible* was used for the Scripture in this para-
graph.)

When man is ill, he can recover through the fragmentation medicine which typifies today's average medical
practice. Such medical practice breaks down when the
illness is beyond its knowledge, for example, terminal
cancer, multiple myeloma, advancing multiple sclerosis,
and many other similar conditions. The new medicine
which was first spoken of by Tournier and alluded to by
Dr. Viktor Frankl, logo-psychosomatic medicine, does
not break down under such circumstances but becomes
even more potent and real. The doctor who wishes to
attend the whole patient certainly does not summon another physician, or even a minister or a prayer group, to
pray for his patient until he himself has ministered to
his patient's spirit. That there is truly a ministry in the
practice of medicine is even spoken of in the "Principles
of Medical Ethics of the American Medical Association," 1949 Edition, page 4: "The profession of medi-

cine, having for its end the common good of mankind, knows nothing of national enmities, of political strife, of sectarian dissensions. Disease and pain the sole conditions of its *ministry*, it is disquieted by no misgivings concerning the justice and honesty of its clients' cause, but dispenses its peculiar benefits, without stint or scruple, to men of every country, and party and rank, and religion, and to men of no religion at all." It is thus seen, in the principles of medical ethics, that medicine is truly a ministry and as its ministry is given out to people of all sorts, that it is the common good of mankind which is being sought and there are no conditions to this ministry except the fundamental needs of the sick patient.

Regarding expansion of the ministry to the whole patient, there are some areas of difficulty when it is necessary to call in spiritual help from chaplain, minister, or prayer group. Possibly, well-meaning attempts of people lacking medical orientation may actually do harm; alarm or concern can be injected as a result of honest attempts to be helpful. Such dangers could be avoided if those wishing to pray, whether layman or minister, would contact the patient's physician for advice and suggestions. As medicine is practiced today, there would be certain misunderstandings, but as medicine grows in the direction of the spiritual, the physician will find that he can be of great assistance to the minister if he will but take a small amount of his time to orient him toward the patient's needs. Certainly, the physician is the one who is oriented toward the needs of the whole patient, and if anyone is going to pray, it truly should be he, if he indeed has the spiritual orientation and the conviction that ". . . with God nothing shall be impossible" (Luke 1:37).

This is a different sort of discipline than writing out a prescription or applying a bandage, carrying out a surgical operation, or administering shock therapy. There is a deep personal involvement of the physician with his patient on the level of the spiritual with consequent effects upon the mind and body. This is present whether the physician or surgeon chooses to recognize it or not. The conscious involvement of the physician on the level of the spiritual carries with it a far deeper implication than the calling in of a clergyman to pray or to administer sacraments. It is a tremendous bolstering of the faith of the patient when the physician gives credence to the power of God and the power of prayer. Such an act or statement of belief on the part of the doctor does much to bolster the patient's faith and can carry him through any trial no matter how serious the course that lies ahead.

As the team of physician, psychiatrist, and clergyman ministers to whole man, the place of the clergyman and others must be considered. "Others" would include those laymen having a true ministry of intercession and prayer for the sick. Those who would desire to minister to the sick should be oriented to basic psychological needs of the patient; they should be sensitive to the status of the patient, both physically and psychologically. In recent years there have been institutes of pastoral care established in major medical centers where hospital chaplains teach clergymen and certain laymen the art of ministering to sick patients. This is a great step in the right direction but still there are many who come uninstructed to minister spiritually to the patient. Strangely enough the ministry of the uninstructed very often carries the potential of more good for the patient than the ministry of those who have had much instruction. The

reason for this may be that instruction carries with it the
potential of a diluting of the faith of the minister to the
point where he develops a greater belief in medical
science than he does in his spiritual ministration. This
has been my personal observation. The minister needs
to see that he has truly a field of his own in which his
duty is simply to present Jesus Christ and the power of
His Holy Spirit to the sick patient. It is not his place to
fill in for the psychiatrist nor to give medical advice. He
is not to prognosticate nor to carry sorrow or worry to
the patient. He must carry joy, confidence, and hope
which are the normal attributes of the ministry of Jesus
Christ. The various ministrations carried out towards
the patient will vary according to religious practice. As
a physician, it is my conviction that the method of ministry is of little concern as long as the minister or the
person who is praying remembers that it is not the ministration or the method which heals or gives solace, but
is the presence of Jesus Christ in the act of prayer or in
the visit itself which is of primary importance.

In many churches there are what are called healing
services, in which various methods of ministering to the
patient are practiced. The physician should be aware of
these services and their potential benefit for his patient.
If medicine in general were more cognizant of such
ministries and areas of help for the patient, they would
be utilized more frequently. The healing services of the
church, whether they be prayer, anointing with oil, or
the laying on of hands or spiritual counsel, are all Scriptural methods which are legitimate and proper. Again,
they should be utilized by those ministers who have
deep discernment of the physical and psychological as
well as the spiritual needs of those who come to them.
The area of cooperation and working together which is

needed in medicine today is not just one of hospital ministry but likewise is needed in situations where the patient is out of the hospital. The enlightened physician may find that his own personal attendance in the church at the time of healing services may be of great strength and benefit to his patients who attend such services.

Reverence is a needed virtue in life today, especially in medicine and nursing. Surgeons are familiar with this virtue in what is termed "reverence for tissue." Reverence for tissue is that type of surgical technique which handles the tissues of the body at the time of surgery with great delicacy, avoiding injury and trauma at the time of an operation. A surgeon with reverence for tissue has patients who do well following surgery and who do not have the stormy, difficult, post-operative courses of patients treated by surgeons who are rough and indelicate in their handling of the body tissues. How can there be reverence for tissue if there is not reverence for the human being, and how can there be reverence for the human being, if there is not reverence for God? Many surgeons who have not given deep consideration to these matters have an orientation toward the person of the patient and toward God manifest through their actions, if not through anything which has come forth on the level of their verbal expression. When man sees that through his natural love for his art and his patient, he is close to God, he can embrace Him whom he has known as close friend, with whom he has always worked, not knowing who He was.

It is a common belief on the part of physicians that a consideration of the human being is of absolute importance. On one occasion, when I was a medical student, I was with a group of senior students making rounds with the renowned surgeon, Dr. Frederick Coller. The patient being examined and discussed was on a large, open ward with a screen pulled about her. Approximately twenty medical students and members of the house staff were present. Something was said by one of the residents to Dr. Coller regarding the patient and, with this, the patient began to weep with evidence of great mental anguish. The young physician who was taking care of the patient stood at the patient's side, unable to do anything to give her solace. Dr. Coller looked deeply at his resident surgeon and stated, "It is your duty as a physician to always comfort the patient, so it is your responsibility now to comfort her."

Certainly, with the many successful surgical and technical procedures that we are able to perform on the patient today, there remains always the necessity to give comfort and succor in the times of mental and spiritual torment which invariably go along with any illness, no matter how minor. An illness is always a threat to the person. The only solace to an ill person may be that given by the physician who stands in the position of the comforter. For those physicians, surgeons, and nurses who will read the New Testament from the point of view of the medicine of the whole person, it will be seen that the precepts of the New Testament Christianity are admirably applicable to an enlightened medical, surgical, and psychiatric and nursing practice which gives comfort and solace to the patient in a way not possible through absolute preoccupation in technological considerations which will always be cold and sterile until the person and the spirit are considered. As God through Jesus Christ enters the heart of doctor and nurse, and as medicine, psychiatry, and the holy ministry unite in caring for the sick and hopeless, the fragmentation of man will cease and not only will man become whole, but those who minister to the sick will, also! "That they may be one, as we are" (John 17:11).

Where there is no vision, the people perish Proverbs 29:18.

12-The Experiment

IN THE LABORATORIES of hospitals and institutions across the world, many varying experiments are being conducted in an attempt to study man and various aspects of man's disease and its treatment. More research is being conducted now than at any former time. As the results of this massive research are made known and as they are applied to patients, man should become healthier. As these advances are made daily, they are often applied in situations which are inadequate, ofttimes disturbing and not always health-producing. With all medical and laboratory factors controlled and superior in quality, the patient can find himself displeased, anxious, and unable to become well—because of the hospital environment. An experiment in hospital patient care has been needed which applies the principles of the Medicine of the Whole Person.

It became apparent several years ago to some of us

that there should be a hospital in which a new type of basic orientation of the facility itself should be attempted. Such a hospital would be oriented to a deeper concept and discipline of medicine through a total belief in caring not only for patients physically and psychologically but also spiritually. Such a hospital, it was theorized, should be centered in the Person of Jesus Christ and the power of His Holy Spirit.

Concerning hospital staff, the personnel in all departments should be oriented toward Christian principles and this should be true, not only in all of the nursing divisions, but also in the orderlies, nurses' aids, diet kitchen, and ancillary services, including laboratory, X ray and physical medicine. It was also seen that the personnel in the business office in administration as well as the medical staff required a similar orientation toward a deeper consideration of the patient than is ordinarily understood. This orientation should be *lived* on the part of the personnel of the hospital in every activity, placing the patient in the position of primary consideration.

Such a hospital would possess an atmosphere of care and concern which should be the atmosphere in which healing could best be achieved. An attempt should be made to keep out such noisiness as television and radio. Noisy patients should be isolated where they do not disturb others. Loud talking and anything disturbing should not be allowed. The use of music would be vital. Music should be carefully screened to insure a salutary and comforting rather than upsetting effect.

Chapel services should be held in the hospital and open to all patients with no attempt to point the patient in the direction of any one religious denomination. In the chapel services the truth in the New Testament concerning Jesus Christ and the power of the Holy Spirit should be considered primary. In conjunction with the chapel a library should be a vital part of the hospital. There such decor as a fireplace and a comfortable lounging area should be provided so patients can be quiet and comfortable in a home-like atmosphere. Meticulous cleanliness must be absolutely essential. Even though the patients are many times elderly and victims of strokes and neurological disease, the odors of such illnesses should be eliminated through absolute cleanliness and through the use of air filtration mechanisms.

Hospital personnel of such a hospital should receive instruction that they should present Jesus Christ to the patient not through verbal expression necessarily, but more through what their eyes and their hands and their attitudes speak. The Bible should be present on every bedside stand for every patient to read, but Christianity should not be forced upon the patient. As the patient begins to wonder why the hospital is different and why there is so much love and care and general improvement in his condition, he will naturally be led to ask what the difference is.

Vital physical medicine is also a necessity wherein not only the usual types of therapy would be utilized, but such therapy would be given with prayer and with a concern for the spiritual being of each patient. Patients' rooms should be accessible to the out-of-doors, to fresh air and sunshine, and gardens, and every room requires decoration with soothing colors and those which bring comfort and happiness to the patient.

Such a hospital did indeed come into existence as Christian Medical Foundation, Incorporated, administered a new convalescent and rehabilitation facility in Medford, Oregon, in 1964. For two years, Christian Medical Foundation, through staffing and through bringing about the conditions described above, was able to perform an unusual ministry to patients, many of whom were considered medically and surgically hopeless. This experiment was not carried out in a laboratory or in a large university center. It was an experiment in the Medicine of the Whole Person, carried out because many consecrated and dedicated people wanted to see if it would be possible in our time to create a hospital for the whole person. In the two years of this experiment, it was proved that such a hospital is feasible and can produce astounding improvement in patients who, to all intents and purposes, are hopelessly, chronically, and terminally ill.

Various examples of this could be cited, but certain cases were outstanding. Although it is difficult to make a statistical measurement of such factors, the clinical improvement of patients in the categories represented is significant. One patient dying of cancer of the breast was almost comatose at the time of admission to the hospital; she remarked to her husband shortly after entering the hospital room, "Oh, I like it here." She then lapsed back into deep coma. The nurses and hospital personnel who cared for the patient talked to her even though she was unconscious and encouraged her not only insofar as her physical being was concerned, but also spiritually. She was surrounded and uplifted on the arms of absolute care and total concern. She was the center of prayer on the part of the entire hospital as morning prayers were said, and as the personnel performed their duties of the day. Within a short time, the patient came out of coma and gradually, despite the generalized spread of cancer through her body, became well enough and strong enough to insist upon going home. This patient was brought to the hospital to die, but something happened as a result of the care and loving concern manifested toward her so that she did not die, but developed great peace, and a lack of pain which had been severe prior to her admission to the hospital. Even though the patient ultimately died, she never had a recurrence of pain, and it was never necessary for her to re-enter the hospital.

Another terminal cancer patient who was admitted for care became progressively more and more interested in what it was that she felt in the atmosphere of the hospital. On one occasion she said, "If I could only reach out and touch what I feel to be present here, I know that I would be healed."

A patient who had cancer was admitted to the hospital for "terminal care." She was extremely depressed and without hope. As she entered her room she requested that the curtains and drapes be drawn to keep the room dark. She spent most of her time in bed and was very quiet, tending to spend much of her time in sleep. As the staff ministered to her, not in words but in acts and in being, and as the atmosphere of the hospital became one which surrounded her with love and care and peace, the patient began to open her drapes and take notice of the flowers and the garden and the beauty of the surrounding countryside. Day by day, instead of getting worse, she became better. On one occasion a member of the family came to the hospital administrator and in great concern said that he did not know what we were doing to his mother-in-law, but he wanted it stopped because he and all of the members of the family had been informed and were aware that the patient was going to die and they expected this. The patient expected this and they did not want her to come out of the hospital only to get sick again and die later. When it was explained to the man that nothing was being done except to surround the patient with loving care, he became pacified. Gradually, as the family became aware that the patient's general health and attitude were those of wholeness rather than illness, their despair and anxiety turned to joy. At this time, the patient requested to be discharged from the hospital and was sent home. Her eventual outcome is unknown at this writing but suffice it to say that in this instance, as in other instances, those patients who came to the hospital in despair and terminal, found life and hope as the healing love of Christ was presented to them. No cancer chemotherapy or other modes of specific medical treatment were utilized in the hospital since patients receiving such therapy were transferred to other facilities. The only modalities of therapy administered to patients in the hospital were excellent nursing care, adequate diet, and the ordinary medications for pain relief and tranquilization as ordered by the personal physician of each patient.

At the time that Christian Medical Foundation began its experiment at the hospital, there was a young man who had been in various hospitals approximately five years. This young man, in his early twenties, had been in a truck struck by a train. He suffered severe brain damage and multiple extreme injuries. When first seen, he was bedridden and emaciated. There was very little ability to communicate on any level and he was basically in a state of increasing "vegetation."

As a result of the constant care and concern on the part of the dedicated nursing staff, the patient gradually was able to be taken out of bed. Through the efforts of the nurses, it was not long before he was able to stand and be fitted with a brace and then to begin to ambulate. His entire being at the time of our first contact with him bespoke of catabolism, the tearing down or breaking down of the body structure. Through love, total care, and proper diet, soon the emaciation had disappeared and his body configuration and general attitude bespoke anabolism, or the building up of his body structure.

Certainly, one of the great anabolic factors in healing is love and hope and the knowledge that somebody cares. To be left in a bed with the prospect of death with no hope is a tremendous catabolic, or destructive, influence upon the body and mind.

One day an elderly woman was admitted who was extremely irrational and unmanageable. Because of her noisiness and confusion, she had to be placed in a quiet room where she would disturb no one. It was necessary to secure the door to her room at all times. In an attempt to get out, she would spend long periods of time pounding at the window with her slipper. She successfully managed to remove the sliding doors of her closet and everything that was not absolutely secured in the room was soon torn apart.

This patient was the grandmother of a minister's wife who had brought her to the hospital, feeling that the ministry of Christian healing could help her. During the patient's early hospital stay, she was the subject of constant prayer endeavor on the part of the hospital staff. Nothing was done in this regard to the patient in a direct manner; she was simply held up in prayer constantly by everyone of the hospital personnel. Gradually it became apparent that she was becoming more tranquil; soon she stopped all noisiness and became quiet and spent most of her time quietly singing to herself and praying. No shock therapy or drug therapy was necessary. In fact, the drugs which were prescribed at the beginning of her hospital course were gradually discontinued and as they were discontinued, the patient became more peaceful. In her instance, it was demonstrated that prayer and loving concern on the part of the hospital staff can calm even a disturbed, senile patient.

There were many instances of patients who came into the hospital for terminal care, distraught and full of fear at the time of their entry. One elderly man with cancer of the lung entered in this frame of mind. Gradually, as he was surrounded by the atmosphere of the hospital, he became peaceful and quiet. He asked for help from one of the nurses. The nurse told him what it was that was different about the hospital and he made the comment that if this was what Christianity was, he wanted to know more about Jesus Christ. He soon became a Christian and became "born of the Spirit." As this occurred, his need for medication became minimal and even though physical healing of his illness did not occur, he became a whole person and died in peace without fear.

Many of the patients in such a hospital are those who are elderly and at times senile. It was noted that, as these patients were placed in an atmosphere of peace, where they were surrounded by beauty, their agitation and disturbance became less and less apparent. In many instances, these patients became wonderfully adjusted and presented none of the problems which had been present before entering the hospital. They were able to participate in occupational therapy activities and were vitally interested in the meetings in the chapel and in the discussion groups. These patients who are of increasing concern in American medicine today cannot be helped in the ordinary nursing home situation. However, in such an atmosphere as was present at the Christian Medical Foundation Hospital in Medford, there was in all instances an absolute improvement in patients cared for by the staff with this new and vital concept of medical and nursing care.

Although it it impossible to give a statistical analysis of all of the cases which were cared for during the period of the experiment, it is my conclusion that Medicine of the Whole Person, in such a hospital situation, albeit one where at times the most difficult type of patients were being cared for, is a type of medical and nursing practice which is extremely salutary and productive of healing. This is an absolute departure from what is seen in the average hospital today where, as the scientific aspect of medicine becomes more and more pronounced, the patient becomes just a small part of a great machine which places him in the center of frenetic and often destructive activities. The sick patient needs to be surrounded with peace and love, not the multiple activities so common in most hospitals today. This is not to say that it is not necessary for there to be the multiple analyses, studies, and therapies that are carried out in hospitals. However, there are varying degrees of illness. In acute illness, many diagnostic studies must be carried out and many activities be concentrated upon the patient. However, as soon as it is possible, it is of utmost importance that the patient be removed from the busy hospital into situations where a more normal and healthful atmosphere can surround him. If this atmosphere can be Christian, with an emphasis on the Medicine of the Whole Person, recovery on all levels of the being will be found to be more rapid than usual. Such an experiment has indeed been carried out in the Medford hospital, and, as a result of almost two year's study of this type of medicine, one can conclude that such medical and nursing practice in enlightened hospitals for the terminally and critically ill can be recommended to American medicine and nursing today.

It is important that as a result of the studies carried out in this experiment, American medicine and nursing come to the realization that the nursing home or convalescent hospital image must be changed. In the medicine of the future, it is postulated that there will be an increasing amount of truly acute care carried out in the large hospital situations. Just as there are now post-anaesthesia recovery rooms and intensive care units, gradually as the pattern emerges there will be areas in hospitals for the care of patients with acute cardiac conditions such as myocardial infarcts (heart attacks), acute cerebrovascular accidents, pulmonary emboli, and acute renal problems such as those patients who require dialysis and other forms of acute medical care. As soon as the patient is able to be moved out of the situation where acute care is needed, he then can be placed in a situation which is more normal and more like the home situation. There are hospitals which have been constructed with this attitude in mind which have been notably successful. The nursing home which altogether too often is a place where senile patients are institutionalized to await death are a relic of the age of neglect of elderly and dying patients. Such facilities should be entirely eliminated from the American medical scene. With the establishment of government programs for medical care of the elderly, many physicians sincerely hope that excellent medical care can be given to all patients no matter what their age or how debilitated, or senile, or chronic they may be. The experiment at the Medford hospital pointed out that such patients can improve tremendously when they are treated as human beings, particularly from the standpoint of Christian care and concern. Such experiments need to be carried out in other situations as a new and enlightened type of care of the elderly, the senile, and the terminally ill appears in American medicine and nursing today aided by government programs.

One of the rarely considered aspects of medical and nursing care is that aspect of patient care which has to do with the patient himself. Too often our evaluation of the patient is a statistical one; that is to say, how many days he has been in the hospital, how much of a certain medication he has been given, what his response has been, et cetera. Many times it is a matter of what kind of an operation has been done and whether or not there has been a recurrence of the problem and how long it has been before the recurrence becomes apparent. There is a continuing need for there to be an analysis of the response of the patient to the care he receives in the hospital. There also should be more thorough evaluation of the patient's attitude and reaction to medication. Simply because medication can be prescribed and given, does not mean that such medication is always good or carries with it the possibility of ultimate benefit. A letter in *The Lancet,* (February 12, 1966) entitled, "What the Patient Felt" has to do with the patient's evaluation of his hospital and medical care during a time when he had a nervous breakdown. Some of the remarks made by the patient are of interest.

> After my nervous breakdown, I was in the hospital for several weeks and I was treated with electric shock and drugs. I don't know whether I am supposed to, but I remember almost every detail and experience.
> I was chiefly struck by the godlike detachment

of the hospital psychiatrists. To be fair, this varied from man to man, but I got the impression that by and large they thought they could cure anything with drugs and shock, in much the same way as a mechanic tackles engine repair. The atmosphere of the place was such that once I began to recover, I tried to get out as quickly as possible even though I was conscious of not being myself. . . .

On the effect of the drugs I was given, I am more sure of my ground. The worst part of the experience was when I began to recover. I could not concentrate for two minutes together. I could neither read nor follow the television. Occupational therapy needed a tremendous effort —not the actual work, but to take an interest in it. On the other hand, just sitting doing nothing brought no relief. The days dragged terribly. The drugs were apparently tranquilizers, but I certainly did not feel tranquil in the sense of being at peace with the world. It was a sort of a frustration, but what it was I wanted to do, I do not know.

Eventually I found that the best thing was to be doing something which needed absolutely no mental effort. I got into a ritual which seemed to help. I voluntarily mopped the washrooms every morning, polishing the taps, and so forth. I made a point of washing and drying the cutlery. I went for frequent walks. We were supposed to stay in the grounds, but I got several miles away at times. I became quite fond of certain walks on the moors. Looking out for certain objects seemed to engage my attention without requiring effort.

When I was discharged, I still had this terrible feeling. Quite how the doctors decide you are "cured" is a mystery to me. It seems to depend on how many electric shocks you have had. How they decide the particular number of shocks is also a mystery. It seems an arbitrary, ritualistic system to me. Once a week the head doctor came around, an occasion of some importance in the hospital life. Since I wanted to get out quickly, I never answered anything but "fine" when asked how I felt. This was my only direct contact with the medical staff.

From the time I went into the hospital I had been taking some sixteen pills a day. After six weeks at home I suddenly decided that I would stop taking the pills and see what happened. I had a few rough nights, but there was an immediate improvement. I felt more like my old self. Within a week I could read for pleasure. I could just jog along as of old without having to force myself into taking an interest in life. Perhaps this feeling was some peculiar reaction to the drug not experienced by others, but I do not think so. . . .

I hope you don't feel I am making a specific complaint against the hospital. I was in a very bad way and I am grateful to the people who looked after me. It cannot be an easy job. But I feel that I have had to drag myself back into normal life in a way that would not have been necessary if there had been more sympathetic contact with the doctors and less blind faith in drugs and shock.

I do not suppose many psychiatrists have had breakdowns. A patient is not likely to connect his lack of concentration with the drug until he stops taking it.

All in all, I am doubtful whether these drugs are really understood. Certainly a drugged patient behaves very quietly and appears very calm, but in my experience the mental torment is worse than at the height of the delirium. Then your thoughts race, but you are only half aware that you are ill. Later, you are fully conscious of your illness but can do nothing about it. You have no thoughts; you lead a sort of suspended, frustrating existence. The only reason you are quiet is because you don't know what the devil to do with yourself. Some sign from the doctors that they understand how you feel would be a great help. As it is, it seems that they have no idea—and if so, how can they really know what they are treating? No doubt many of these impressions were affected by my illness and were illogical. Nonetheless, it is how I felt which matters.

Were patients more often to relate their experiences in hospitals and with doctors and nurses and were the medical and nursing professions to take cognizance of such writings, there would be an improvement in patient care in general. However, we tend to live in a state of detachment from the patient and from the hospital situation. It is necessary for the doctor and the nurse to look more thoroughly at the hospital itself. Not just the laboratory or its operating room, or delivery room, or intensive care unit, but the hospital rooms and corridors and the general aspect of the place in which our patients must live. Were we to do this, we would see that such an experiment as was carried out in Medford indeed was one which bears repetition on the scale of larger institutions.

We who profess and call ourselves Christians must see that there should be no difference whatsoever between Christian care and medical and nursing care in general. Certainly, American medicine as it exists at present is an outgrowth of Christian concern for people. Many of our hospitals were established by Christian denominational groups. Somehow, however, we have removed God and Jesus Christ from our consideration. We have become atheistic without realizing it. As long as we practice medicine and nursing without the consideration of God and with no mention of Him, we are basically atheistic whether we choose to actually define ourselves so or not.

American medicine today, by and large, is perhaps as atheistic as Soviet medicine. The only difference is that Russians realize and profess their atheism, and we have developed our atheism by secondary intention. Such medicine and nursing practice is sterile and not considerate of the deeper aspects of the life of the patient wherein lies not only his true inner spirit and psychological being but also the key to his recovery and his wholeness not only while he is in the hospital, but more especially when he is discharged for care as an outpatient and at home. The few cases cited in the hospital experiment in Medford can serve only as a guideline to a more enlightened medical and nursing practice of the future.

It is appropriate in American medicine that now when great strides are being taken in care of the elderly, many of them chronically and terminally ill, for the Medicine of the Whole Person to be the rule of future practice, rather than the exception.

In considering the patient and his reaction to hospitalization and illness in general, there is needed a Patient's Bill of Rights:

1. The patient has the right to know that he will receive the highest and best nursing and medical care available in order to achieve care and consideration of his spirit, soul, and body.

2. He needs to know that the nursing and medical profession who care for him are qualified through education, experience, and character to carry out the services for which they are responsible.

3. The patient needs to know that the medical and nursing personnel caring for him will be sensitive to his feelings and responsive to his total needs as a person.

4. That within limits determined by his physician, the patient and his family will be taught about the illness besetting the patient, so that he can help himself, and his family can understand and help him after his discharge from the hospital.

5. That plans will be made with him and his family, or, if necessary, for him, so that continuing care be available to him throughout the entire period of his need.

6. That adequate records be kept and that con-

fidence be maintained concerning the character of his illness.

7. That a healthful environment be around him in the hospital—an environment which conveys an atmosphere itself conducive to healing.

8. That while he is being treated in mind and body, his spiritual needs also be considered and that if he should be facing death, he may have the opportunity to accept Jesus Christ as his Saviour through the combined efforts of the doctor, nurse, and minister.

9. That though he be in coma, or anaesthetized, or otherwise without consciousness, he always be treated with love and dignity.

10. That although minority beliefs and practices be always honored and preserved, the right of the Christian to be treated according to the tenets of his Christian belief be also honored, preserved, and practiced.

11. That the patient has the right to know that no matter how critical his situation may be, he never will be denied hope.

A new heart also will I give you, and a new spirit will I put within you: and I will take away the stony heart out of your flesh, and I will give you an heart of flesh Ezekiel 36:26.

13-A New Heart

ONTO THE WORLD'S surgical and scientific scene there has recently come the startling phenomenon of the removal of various parts of the body from deceased persons and the re-implantation of organs into patients dying for the lack of healthy organs. The most recent accomplishments have been the transplantation of the heart, lung, liver, and the pancreas. In a recent book on organ transplantation, the surgeon gives various quotations at the beginning of each chapter. There is one quotation taken from the Holy Bible and it is interesting that it is one of the few quotations of Satan, "skin for skin, yea, all that a man hath will he give for his life" (Job 2:4). Why this particular quotation was used is difficult to say, except that it does reflect a prophetic truth despite its origin. Man will do anything in order to preserve his temporal life despite the fact that there is the promise of God that he will have life eternal through belief in Jesus Christ.

Surgeons will be required in time to come to think more deeply on moral questions than even the theologian or the Christian moralist, since ultimately it is the surgeon who must make the decision to operate and to transplant. It is his hands which do the final act of removing an organ from one individual and transplanting it into another. There are those who would place the physician in the capacity of a technician operating at the bid and call of a board of experts. This concept is loathsome to the surgeon who realizes that his occupation is hardly that of a technician or a carpenter, but is indeed a holy calling given to him by God with all of its awesome responsibility.

A reporter asked a famous American surgeon who has done a number of transplants his opinion of families who refuse permission for the heart to be taken from a loved one to be transplanted into another individual. The doctor said he found such an attitude incomprehensible. He felt that donation of organs should be allowed in every instance. The reporter asked him if the refusal to grant the organ for transplantation were based upon a religious consideration, i.e., that the heart was the seat of the soul. The doctor replied that this *had* been the consideration. It was his feeling that "*if there is a soul,* it is located in the head and not in the heart."

The purpose of relating this event is simply to point out the fact that now, more than ever, surgeons are having to give consideration to moral and religious questions. Since theirs is the ultimate decision as to whether such operations are to be performed, the education of future physicians and surgeons must not exclude the field of Christian ethics and decision making.

In considering organ transplantation, there is an often-ignored, but all-important, question which must be answered in every instance. Does the potential donor have any chance of survival? Several years ago I was requested to see a young girl who had sustained a cardiac arrest and who had been unconscious for three months. During that time she had been seen by many physicians and specialists; all had concurred: no possibility of recovery. I was asked to see her, not only from the medical standpoint but also because as a Christian doctor, perhaps I might see her situation from the viewpoint of Christian hope. Entering the hospital room, I was overwhelmed by a picture of complete despair and hopelessness. The child herself was what medicine calls a "vegetable." Everyone surrounding her was devoid of hope. Such a patient at such a point could conceivably be considered for organ donation. Most of those surrounding her at the time of my visit were of an opinion that she should be allowed to die. Our decision was to pray and to ask God to heal her. We also made the decision to surround her with love and care, concern and hope. With these as our only *armamentaria,* the child began to respond. Within a few months she was discharged from the hospital.

The decision to carry out organ transplantation must always be done with the knowledge that the person receiving the transplanted organ may die during or shortly after the procedure. The individual who is to be the donor must possess living, healthy organs in order for them to be successfully implanted. Thus the donor must, in a certain sense, be living at the time the organs are removed. By older criteria of death, his respirations have not ceased nor has his heart stopped beating. The brain waves may be "flat," but by these new criteria of death, doctors are apt to substitute the findings of a *diagnostic instrument* for clinical diagnosis. In a sense, the donor must die in order for the recipient to have an opportunity to live. Therefore, there must be great concern and thorough and exhaustive consultation before deciding to allow a person to be a donor. Such operations should only be done at specified centers where there is every facility available for deep moral as well as scientific decisions.

In all instances, the donor is someone who has met with some sort of catastrophe—whether it be an accident or attempted suicide. With the advent of resuscitation methods, such an unfortunate individual may be brought into a hospital emergency service in a state of apparent death. He is then resuscitated and brought back to life so that his heart and vital organs are functioning, excepting perhaps the brain. Were he to live, it is entirely possible that he would live in a state of vegetation for a matter of weeks, months, or years, never regaining consciousness.

There are those instances, however, where people in a state of vegetation have recovered despite every prognostication to the contrary. Thus, the transplant surgeon is faced with a dilemma in which he must obtain the consultation and advice of his fellow physicians and hopefully, the best minds of men who think upon man not only physically, but spiritually.

It is a Christian principle that the giving up of one's life so that another may live is a manifestation of great love. Jesus Christ said, "Greater love hath no man than this, that a man lay down his life for his friends" (John 15:13). It is a matter of tremendous and soul-searching importance to the individual who has received a transplanted heart as he contemplates the fact that he owes his life not only to the skill and scientific acumen of a number of excellent surgeons, but also that he carries within his being the heart of an individual who died in order that he might live. It is the opinion of such patients that transplant operations are of absolute importance. Certainly their life has depended upon the success of such an operation.

Thus it can be recommended: in order to help to give life to certain productive and critically ill individuals who otherwise face certain death, organ transplantation should be considered. Such operations should never become commonplace. The decisions involved should be based upon the deepest of moral and ethical considerations.

In order to utilize every ethical safeguard, such operations should only be done where the ultimate consideration of all factors is available. The least of these is technical ability to perform the operation. Surgeons performing such operations should be expert not only in technical phases of operative procedure and after-care, but they should be more thoroughly grounded than other physicians in psychological and spiritual considerations of such operative procedures.

The transplant surgeon should have the knowledge, in talking with the family of a prospective donor, that the soul is not located in the heart; nor is it located in the head. The soul is, in fact, the thinking and understanding part of the individual present in all areas of his consciousness. The heart has been called the seat of the understanding (soul). In this instance it does not mean the heart as we understand it but the inner part of one's being.

Thus, in transplanting a heart, there is no transplantation of soul or spirit, but of a physical organ. When the patient has had a severe brain injury—either due to a prolonged lack of oxygen to the brain or a destructive accident which has destroyed the thinking part of the brain—this will be manifested on the electroencephalogram by a characteristic electric pattern. Under these circumstances, the understanding of the individual which includes his will and those attributes of his personality or self are no longer present nor are they retrievable. If one can be certain of this fact, one can with certainty go ahead with the removal of the donor organ or organs if the family allows the organ donation to be done.

The other and perhaps most difficult question is: when does the spirit leave the body? Is the eternal spirit of the individual gone at the moment the soul succumbs? This is doubtless something that we shall never know exactly. However, it is my contention that whatever surgical procedure I am involved in, I shall always consider the patient as spiritually aware of what is happening, whether or not he is conscious. If it is impossible to anaesthetize the spirit, it is also impossible to destroy the spirit through an accident or through suicide.

It is possible that the third part of man—his spirit— is present in the donor, even at the moment of organ donation. Total physical death ensues at the moment of the organ donation; it is doubtless true that the spirit, if it has not gone to be with God prior to that time, departs at that moment. For the person who is in Christ, this is not a moment to be considered with anxiety or fear, but for the person who is not in Christ, it is indeed a tragic moment. It also would behoove the surgeon who is involved in this moral and ethical problem to be very sure of his ground, spiritually. I would not want to ever make any of these decisions apart from an attitude of prayer and the deepest searching of the guidance and direction of God with reference to the proposed procedure. This should be done in every instance. The era of organ transplantation makes it imperative that the surgeon, perhaps more than any other mortal man at this time, must be a man not only of the mind and the soul, but also of the Spirit.

But my God shall supply all your need according to his riches in glory by Christ Jesus Philippians 4:19.

14-Prayer

GOD IS NOT limited by the limitations of the minds of men. The Bible promises that God will supply all our needs through Christ Jesus. This does not allow for any limitation or exception. When Jesus Christ lived here on earth He taught men to live in a new dimension of prayer and expectancy. He did not allow anything on the level of the impossible to deter Him or to stop His ministry to the sick. Not even death was able to defeat Him. He demonstrated in the raising of Lazarus that if the need were for one to be raised from the dead, God can indeed supply that need. With men there are many impossibilities, but ". . . with God all things are possible" (Mark 10:27).

One of the things which characterizes the practice of surgery is the presence of those patients for whom it is impossible to become well or to totally recover from their illnesses. As one makes his rounds in various hospitals, he cannot help but be aware that many of those whom he sees from day to day—both his own patients and others'—are facing imminent death. A hospital is a strange mixture of those who are being preserved for further life and those who are in the acute process of dying. Impossibility lies on every hand. The doctor and the nurse learn to live in this reality.

One night I visited the intensive care unit of one of our local hospitals. My patient had cancer; and following radical surgery she was lingering between life and death. A tube was in her throat, and she was unable to talk. However, she wrote a brief note—"Pray for me"—and grasped my hand. There in the midst of many others in similar situations, with background sounds of cardiac monitors beeping, occasional desperate cries of patients, and the reassuring replies of nurses, we prayed, asking God to intervene. My patient immediately became calm and a new courage could be seen to be emanating from her. As I left her I walked down to the darkened corridors of the hospital. Someone was being taken into the operating room for emergency surgery. Ambulances were bringing other patients into the emergency suite.

I walked by the hospital chapel. No one was there, and its quiet peace summoned me as I slipped inside and lifted up the needs of my patients who were in the hospital that busy night. I also prayed for the physicians and the nurses and asked that God's guiding hand be with them. The chapel seemed like an island of hope in the midst of an ocean of desperation. I breathed a quiet prayer of thanksgiving that someone had had the foresight to see that there was such a place in the hospital for times like this.

After leaving the chapel, I went to visit another patient. Walking down the corridor to see her, I noted on a nearby door a sign "No Ministers Allowed—By Order of the Patient's Doctor." I reflected for a moment as to what such a sign could mean. A nurse, noticing, quietly told me the reason for the sign: the ministers visiting the patient said things such as, "How are you feeling today?" She would reply, "Very well, thank you." Then, "Now, you know that I am a minister so you can be honest with me. How do you *really* feel?" In view of the desperate and terminal cancer, everyone reflected discouragement and despair.

Similar conversations and attitudes—all of them more psychological than spiritual—caused the physician to order that no further negativism be allowed. Such statements and philosophy were adding to the patient's burden, rather than lightening it. I heartily concurred with my fellow surgeon's feelings. Those who visit the sick *must* be conveyors of hope. When one has Jesus Christ's life in him, he can see hope even in the most impossible situation. God is the God of the impossible.

If those who claim to be ministers of the gospel of Jesus Christ cannot encourage, cannot bring faith and hope and healing virtue into sickrooms, they should be forbidden contact with patients. Their place is not to interrogate the patient nor to determine anything concerning the progress of his illness, its physical and psychological attributes.

The minister's primary function is to breathe confidence into the patient's life, to pray for the patient, and give whatever ministrations his denomination prescribes. He should leave the patient uplifted and strengthened as a result of his visit. If he does not believe that God exists, if he feels that God is dead or that

God does not heal or bring hope to the hopeless, he should not visit the sick. His visits can only be detrimental, even if he does not say a word. A defeatest attitude is lethal to the sick patient whether it emanates from minister, doctor, or nurse.

There was a young teen-age girl in our community who was dying of a cancerous growth in her arm which had spread into the axilla and the chest wall. Neighbors of the girl—knowing that I was a physician who believed in the healing ministry of Christ—had asked me if I would visit her to encourage her spiritually, since it was apparent that there was nothing further that could be done for her medically or surgically. I replied that I should be most pleased to visit her if a request for such a visit came from her physician. Shortly thereafter the girl's physician came up to me and asked me, "What do you believe concerning prayer for hopeless patients?" I asked him what he meant. He related that he had been approached by his patient's family and friends regarding having me visit his patient. I explained to him that I had informed them that I would not visit the child unless requested to do so by him. He replied quite indignantly, "I am a Christian and I believe in prayer and if any doctor is going to pray for my patient, I will do the praying!"

I relate this story only to state that I believe absolutely that this physician was correct. In the ideal situation I do not believe that anyone is any closer to the patient than his physician. The minister or priest may not be as close to the patient as the doctor. The doctor who takes care of his patient physically and psychologically is the logical person to take care of him spiritually.

It is unwise to divide the patient into various parts and areas, since he is a unity and must be cared for always as a whole being. Thus, who can better pray for the patient than his concerned physician? Certainly, a physician rather than a clergyman knows the circumstances of the illness, how serious it may be, or its prognosis. Too, a minister's prayers might be misinterpreted by the patient as negative prayers or a form of "last rites." Consider the lethal implication of the prayer for healing "*if* it be Thy will"! The physician should never abandon his patient, even to a minister. The enlightened minister who believes in Christian healing is a wonderful help to patient and physician, but the patient's terminal care spiritually should not be relegated only to him. The doctor or nurse who ignores spiritual involvement with his patient is actually not avoiding the issue. Lack of spiritual care and concern are negativistic and destructive to the patient at a time when this aspect of his care becomes all-important and physical and psychological methods become meaningless and fruitless.

Prayer may not necessarily be verbal. Often it is the unspoken prayer which has the greatest result. One time I was discussing prayer with the German psychiatrist, Von Dürckheim. I asked him what his opinion was concerning prayer for patients in the hospital. He replied to me, "There are times when I may have a patient who is possessed of morbid fear. The patient may be afraid to be alone and afraid to be out of my presence. On such occasions I have seen fit from time to time to sit at the bedside all night, holding the patient's hand and reassuring him that everything is alright. This to me is prayer." He then said that occasionally in his practice his patients may require shock therapy. They are brought back following their treatment and placed in their room. Von Dürckheim spoke of the importance of the *kind of eyes* they would see when awakening from their treatment. Eyes of love, care, and concern differ from those which are impersonal or irritated and upset. One's eyes speak prayer. His attitude bespeaks prayer. A life speaks prayer—or it doesn't. A man is either plus or minus spiritually. He cannot be neutral.

I began to think about Christianity as ordinarily practiced and it occurred to me that Christianity is often a spoken religion. Prayers are those things which are said or read out of a prayer book. Christianity is often conceived as the history detailed in the New Testament, the proclamation that those who believe in Jesus Christ will be saved to life eternal.

However, there is, I am sure, a greater depth and a greater reality to the life of Jesus Christ who lives within the believer. It cannot be just what is being said or just what is being proclaimed in the pulpit or in the witness at the Christian Men's Club. It must be something that is being *lived,* not in the power of the individual, but in the power of Jesus' Resurrection. Such a *living faith* in the sick room and in the psychiatric wards is needed in all of those places where the sick person longs not just to *hear* a prayer but to *see* vital, quickening Christianity lived and practiced in the lives of those who care for him in his hour of need.

Were this to be the case there would be no need for signs to be placed on patients' doors saying, "No Ministers Allowed." This is a dimension of Christian hope of which the physician and the nurse are perhaps better qualified to evaluate and be a part than anyone else. They are on the front lines fighting against death and disease. The physician perhaps more than most other mortal men, needs the strengthening power of the Holy Spirit and the virtue of Jesus Christ in his life. Alone he is constantly being sapped of healing virtue. He is a channel of the healing love of God through Jesus Christ whether he chooses to believe this fact or not. He has the gift of healing which is a gift of God and the Holy Spirit, whether he has ever accepted the precepts of Christianity or not. How much greater his results would be, not only on the temporal but on the eternal scale, if he were to see that he is indeed a co-laborer with God as he goes about his daily endeavors in the healing of the sick. He would then have a constant and ever-increasing supply of compassion, love, and strength in order to meet the myriad needs of the multitudes of sick whom he sees every day. The physician cannot carry all of these burdens alone, but with the power of Christ indwelling, he will find that he has a new strength and is no longer drained of life and joy and victory as is so often the case when one attempts to heal the sick, relying only on his own human frailty and in the human efforts of those who surround him—however conscientious and however laudable.

My patient in the intensive care suite, following prayer, began to get well and soon was discharged from the hospital. Not only was she healed of the immediate problem, but God has continued to heal her in all areas of her spirit, soul, and body. This truly is the ultimate purpose of the physician's life and of the Christian's life —those who believe in and trust the Lord Jesus Christ. The Christian must uniquely portray the healing power of Christ; otherwise, he is proclaimer of something other than the Gospel. The Gospel message is a healing message and not only are doctors and nurses in need of its possession in their own lives, but man in general in the desperate hour in which we live in the world today needs the healing Gospel of Jesus as in no other previous time.

S-18

From the jungles of Ecuador to a tiny watchshop in Holland to behind the Iron Curtain—thrill to the very real human drama of ordinary people who suddenly find themselves empowered by God's love to do *extraordinary* things . . .

___THROUGH GATES OF SPLENDOR. Five young Americans travel to Ecuador to build bridges: from paganism to Christian belief. *Elliott.* $1.25 paper

___THE HIDING PLACE. A Dutch spinster's world is turned upside down when she begins to hide Jews during World War II. *ten Boom.* $1.50 paper

___GOD'S SMUGGLER. In the face of tremendous odds, one man takes on the daring mission of smuggling Bibles across the Iron Curtain. *Andrew.* 95¢ paper

___THE PERSECUTOR. How a Soviet secret police member comes to embrace the faith of those he formerly persecuted. *Kourdakov.* $1.50 paper

ORDER FROM YOUR BOOKSTORE

If your bookstore does not stock these books, order from
SPIRE BOOKS
Box 150, Old Tappan, New Jersey 07675
Please send me the books I've checked above. Enclosed is my payment plus 25¢ mailing charge on first book ordered, 10¢ each additional book.

NAME_____

STREET_____

CITY_____ STATE_____ ZIP_____

____Amount enclosed. ____Cash. ____Check. ____Money order. (No c.o.d.'s)